How to Raise and Train

P I G E O N S

REVISED and ENLARGED EDITION

By WILLIAM H. ALLEN, Jr.

 STERLING PUBLISHING CO., INC. NEW YORK

 Oak Tree Press Co., Ltd. London & Sydney

OTHER BOOKS OF INTEREST

Bird Life (for Young People)
Cage Bird Identifier
Pigeon Racing

Photographs on pages 1-127
by Louise Brown Van der Meid.

1974 Printing
Copyright © 1972, 1959 by Sterling Publishing Co., Inc.
419 Park Avenue South, New York, N.Y. 10016
British edition published by Oak Tree Press Co., Ltd., Nassau, Bahamas
Distributed in Australia and New Zealand by Oak Tree Press Co., Ltd.,
P.O. Box J34, Brickfield Hill, Sydney 2000, N.S.W.
Distributed in the United Kingdom and elsewhere in the British Commonwealth
by Ward Lock Ltd., 116 Baker Street, London W 1
Manufactured in the United States of America
All rights reserved
Library of Congress Catalog Card No.: 58-7602
Sterling ISBN 0-8069-3706-8 Trade   Oak Tree 7061-2284-4
3707-6 Library

CONTENTS

1. Pigeons as a Hobby

If you want to keep a few pigeons as a hobby, this book is for you. It will introduce you to a few of the various breeds of pigeons that are available and tell you how to care for the breed or breeds of your choice.

WHY KEEP PIGEONS?

I know of no more fascinating hobby than that of pigeon keeping. Thousands of people the world over breed and keep racing homers because they love the pigeons themselves, because they enjoy training them for races and because they enjoy the keen competition of the race itself. Many pigeon racing enthusiasts feel that there is as much satisfaction in raising and training a champion racing pigeon as there is in raising and training a good race horse. Certainly pigeon racing is more nearly within the reach of all than is horse racing. If you enjoy the satisfaction of creating good racing stock and the thrill of competition, then this phase of pigeon keeping should suit you.

Other thousands of people keep pigeons for their beauty and because they enjoy tending and raising beautiful birds. There is a great satisfaction that comes with producing something as lovely as a young pigeon in its first adult feathers. No other bird or animal is produced in such a wide variety of forms and colors, so no matter what your taste, there is sure to be a pigeon that will appeal to you. Almost every variety has its own enthusiastic club of supporters who have set up a standard of excellence for the breed. A pigeon show is often the scene of keen competition between fanciers of the various breeds represented.

If you are looking for a hobby that will also provide some meat for the table, pay for itself, and perhaps earn some extra

You can train your pigeons easily, even getting them to pick grains of corn from between your teeth.

Some pigeon fanciers feel that the thrill of developing new breeds and colors is the most fascinating aspect of the hobby. This fancier is holding a very tame Pouter pigeon.

money as well, you need look no further. Pigeons are doing those things for thousands. Indeed, there are many commercial squab farms that provide their owners with money enough to live on quite comfortably.

Why keep pigeons? There are as many reasons as there are fanciers, but no matter what the reason, the pigeon keeper has one of the most interesting and fascinating hobbies to be found. If you are already a pigeon fancier, you know what I am talking about. If you have not yet fallen under the spell of this absorbing pastime, you are missing one of the most enjoyable experiences of your life.

HISTORY OF PIGEON KEEPING

The keeping of domestic pigeons as a hobby or as a source of profit is by no means new. As a matter of fact, it is one of the oldest hobbies known to man. There are written records of pigeons being kept in the fifth Egyptian dynasty, around 3000 B.C.

There are frequent references to doves (pigeons) in the Bible. They came to have a place in the Hebrew religious ritual, where they were often used as sacrifices to atone for sin. In New Testament times the dove was a symbol for the Holy Spirit.

It is thought that some varieties of the domestic pigeon were brought back to Europe from the East during the Crusades.

Ring-neck doves are believed to be closely related to the common pigeon. However, their manner of flight differs greatly from the racing pigeon.

White doves have been a symbol of peace for centuries. The Greeks
domesticated them over 2,000 years ago!

Since around 1600 pigeons have certainly been domesticated
and have been kept in Europe continuously. For a while only
the aristocrats were allowed the privilege of keeping pigeons
and it was an offense for a peasant to attempt to keep them.
After a time, however, the restrictions were relaxed and the
peasantry began to keep and breed pigeons too.

Pigeons were brought to America during the early years of
its history and have been kept ever since.

It is hard to believe that the many varieties of domestic pigeons are all descended from the same wild ancestor, but such is thought to be the case. The more than 200 varieties of domestic pigeons have probably descended from the Blue Barred Rock Pigeon, *Columba livia*, which is found in the wild state in Europe, Africa and Asia. Many varieties of domestic pigeon resemble their ancestor. Other varieties seem to differ as much from *Columba livia* as they do from others of their domestic cousins. Nevertheless, all the varieties of domestic pigeons will interbreed and their offspring are capable of reproducing themselves.

These Australian Crested Doves are a wild species, but they are adaptable to life in a coop.

Pouter pigeons, like so many of the fancier varieties, are bred for their appearance rather than for their flying ability. They are among the most amusing of all birds, looking for attention as they strut back and forth.

TYPES OF PIGEONS

Today there are three basic classes of pigeons:

1. *Fancy*—Those pigeons that are kept merely as a hobby and are bred for their color and appearance. They are the varieties that are most frequently seen in the pigeon shows and that attract the most attention because of their beautiful or exotic appearance. Each fancy breed has its own admirers and its own standards of excellence that breeders try to work toward in the production of their squabs.

11

2. *Flyers*—Those pigeons, such as racing homers and tumblers, that are kept for their flying ability. Show standards have been set up, but performance is the most important thing to most fanciers and appearance is secondary. The pigeons are bred for their tumbling or flying ability or for their ability to fly long distances and find their home lofts.

3. *Utility*—Those pigeons that are bred for the table. They produce the delicate-flavored squabs that are served in better restaurants and hotel dining rooms. Utility pigeons should grow to a large size, have white skin, and be able to produce nest

These Racing Homers are not valuable for their color patterns nor for their fancy feathering. It is performance that is important. They are bred for their ability to fly fast and true to their home loft after release from a distant point. Pigeon racing is very popular all over the world.

White Fantails are used for many purposes. Because of their beauty they are often kept around mansions and farms solely for decorative purposes, but when food was scarce during the war they were found to be very tasty. Even today a few are still raised for the table.

after nest of young. Good utility pigeons sometimes produce as many as 11 pairs of squabs a year.

These three classes, fancy, flyers, and utility, indicate the primary purpose for which each breed is produced. It does not necessarily mean that any given breed is used exclusively for any one purpose. There is some overlapping, to be sure. The squabs of all classes may be and indeed are eaten, and they are real delicacies. Show standards are set up for practically all breeds, including utility breeds.

The type of pigeon you decide to keep and the purpose for which you keep pigeons will have some bearing upon the accommodations you will provide and upon the general management of your lofts or dovecote. In general, however, the care of all pigeons is very much the same, with the needs of one breed very similar to the needs of other breeds.

Pigeon keeping can cost just about what you want it to. You can buy a pair of pigeons for as little as $2.00 to $3.00 or you can pay several hundred dollars for a champion racing or

Most pigeon fanciers raise pigeons for fun, and profit is secondary. This homemade loft is not luxurious, but it serves its purpose well.

If you hand-feed your pigeons, you will get to know
each other and the birds will become very tame.

exhibition bird. The cost of housing for your pigeons can vary
considerably too. A pair or two of pigeons can be kept in a
simple homemade cage or you can build a fancy loft. More will
be said about accommodations in Chapter 4.

Before you acquire your pigeons, become familiar with the
general principles and problems of keeping them. Later, when
some question regarding pigeons and their care arises, this book
will serve as a ready reference. Use it often, and it will make the
fascinating hobby of pigeon keeping still more absorbing.

2. General Management

After you have decided what type or types of pigeons you want to keep, get the best breeding stock you can afford, even if you can get only one pair. To start with inferior or mediocre breeding stock is to jeopardize your new venture and the enjoyment it will bring you. On the other hand, if you get the best stock available, even though you get few birds, you are starting off right. If you take good care of your birds there is no reason why you should not have a successful hobby that can give you a great deal of pleasure and enjoyment for many years. Feeding and housing your pigeons are discussed in detail in later chapters.

DISTINGUISHING THE SEXES

First, be sure to get true pairs when you get your breeding stock. This may not be as obvious as you might suppose, for it is quite difficult to tell the sex of young pigeons until they are several months old. Even then the sexes can be more easily distinguished by their behavior than by their appearance.

As a general rule, the male tends to be somewhat larger than the female and he usually has a thicker neck. The male is generally more aggressive than the female. One male characteristic that females seldom show is sustained cooing and dancing. Males will often coo at other birds and at the same time dance or turn completely around. Females, although they coo, do not do so as frequently or for as long as the males and seldom dance as the males do.

Even if two pigeons build a nest and attempt to incubate

eggs, they may not be a true pair. It is not uncommon for two pigeons of the same sex, when confined together, to try to set up housekeeping. They may build a nest and, if both are females, they may lay eggs, which, of course, will be infertile. If both are males, even though they may nest, of course there will be no eggs.

Several varieties of pigeons have sex-linked colors that make it easy to tell their sex as soon as they are feathered out. Sex-linkage, however, is a subject to be taken up by the advanced and experienced pigeon fancier and has no place in this basic handbook.

This Scobian is a rare type of fancy pigeon closely related to the Flights, long-faced pigeons with white eyes.

MATING

People often ask, "Do pigeons mate for life?" The answer is that unless they are separated by their keeper or by some other cause they usually do mate for life. If they are separated, however, they will generally accept new mates readily. Unmated mature pigeons may entice away the mate of another pigeon if they have the opportunity to do so. For this reason it is unwise to keep unmated pigeons, either males or females, in the same pen with mated pairs. It is usually safe to keep any number of mated pairs together without fear of their being unfaithful and intermating with one another.

Both male and female pigeons gather nesting material, build the nest, incubate the eggs and care for the young. Usually the male gathers the nesting material and brings it to the female. She weaves it into the nest. The female takes the longest shift at incubating the eggs. She usually sits on the nest from about 4:00 in the afternoon until about 9:00 or 10:00 the next morning. The male incubates the eggs during the day while the hen is off the nest. This provides yet another method of telling the sexes apart. It is the male who is on the nest during the late morning and early afternoon and the female at all other times. When the eggs are hatched both parents help feed the young.

Often by the time the young squabs are feathered out and ready to leave the nest the parents have started another nest and are incubating another clutch of eggs in the other side of the nest box. Good utility pigeons will raise nest after nest in this manner, but usually the breeders of fancy flying or show stock restrict their pigeons to two or three nests per year.

Pigeons become quite attached to their mates and to nesting sites. They will defend either with considerable vigor against intruders or will fly great distances to reach either. It is this attachment to home and family, coupled with an almost unerring sense of direction and homing instinct, that has been cultivated and capitalized upon with the Racing Homer.

Mating is covered in detail in Chapter 6.

CLEANLINESS

Probably the most important single factor in successful pigeon management is cleanliness. Whatever quarters you choose should be kept scrupulously clean. If this precaution is observed, you will probably have very little trouble with insect pests and diseases. At least once a year, remove the pigeons and wash the quarters thoroughly, spray them with insecticide and white-wash or paint them. This may seem a lot of trouble but it is good insurance against disease and insects. You may spread

It is dangerous to feed your pigeons from a dirty pan. Contagious diseases can be spread too easily that way. Cleanliness is extremely important in good pigeon management.

sand or sawdust on the floor of the loft to absorb droppings and to aid in maintaining cleanliness.

After each pair of squabs is hatched, clean out the nest boxes and nesting bowls and sprinkle a little mite powder on the bottom. This will help prevent insect pests.

In addition to the thorough yearly cleaning, regular cleaning is advisable.

Pigeons will keep themselves clean if they are allowed to do so. They love to bathe and should be given the opportunity frequently. This is particularly important in hot weather, but pigeons should have the chance to bathe at least three times a week regardless of the weather or temperature.

The Bald-Headed Tumbler gets its name from its white head with no markings. Some members of the large Tumbler family are still bred for their flying and somersaulting ability.

This Crested or Capped Helmet is also a Tumbler. The "crest" or "cap" refers to the ruffled feathers on the back of the head; the "helmet," of course, is the dark head itself.

The best bathing dishes are flat shallow crockery or earthenware saucers. Empty the bath water after all the pigeons have bathed and supply fresh clean water at the next bath time. Keep the bath water separate from the drinking water.

When the birds are nesting, the bath takes on special significance. The moisture that is carried back to the nest on the pigeon's feathers helps make the eggshell soft and hatchable. Without it the eggshell and inner membranes become tough and the young pigeon is unable to crack the shell and emerge from it when the time comes.

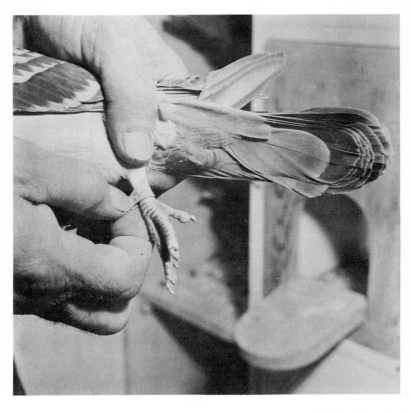

The stretchable band, removable at any time, is useful for keeping mating records. A seamless band is permanent, and can only be put on a very young squab.

BANDING

Many fanciers, particularly those who are breeding pigeons for exhibition or racing purposes, like to band their pigeons. Numbered bands on the legs of your pigeons will certainly help you to keep breeding records. There are two kinds of bands, seamless and open. The seamless band is permanent and must be put on the squab's leg when it is just a few days old. After that the squab's foot grows, the bones in the foot harden and become less pliable, and it is impossible to slip the band on over the toes. A bird wearing a seamless band can always be identified. The band numbers may be registered with the society or club interested in the particular breed of pigeon.

The open band may be put on and removed at any time. It is usually used to keep mating records when a pigeon may have one mate one season, another the next. After each mating the band is taken off.

MOLTING

Molting is a natural process that begins when pigeons are only six or seven weeks old. At this time they shed their juvenile plumage and grow their adult plumage.

Adult pigeons molt annually, usually in late summer and early fall, replacing the old, worn feathers with new ones. Most authorities now agree that molting is not a dangerous period in a pigeon's life if the bird is properly nourished and provided with the materials which build bones and feathers. While most commercial breeders go right on breeding their birds during the molt, breeders of show or racing stock usually time the breeding so that the birds are not raising young during the molt. It is safe, however, to let well-nourished pigeons breed and raise young during that period.

Some breeders like to induce an early molt so that their pigeons will be in full plumage for the early fall shows. They do this by separating the pairs and withholding food for 24 hours or reducing the number of meals from two to one per day, since there seems to be some direct relationship between diet and molt. As soon as the molt is well under way the feeding should be restored to the normal two meals per day.

Molt may be affected by locality, diet, disease, accidental injury or other factors. There may even be considerable difference among different varieties.

3. Varieties of Pigeons

There are more than 200 varieties of pigeons to choose from, of all sizes, shapes and colors. No matter how hard to please you may be, you should be able to find at least one breed to suit your fancy. Although all pigeons are descended from the

The Jacobin on the left is a very valuable and rare specimen. The English Turbit on the right, although not as rare as the Jacobin, is still a beauty. Note the "boots" on the legs of the Turbit.

This Elsinor Roller, a long-faced bird, is particularly valuable for its attractive markings and high flying ability.

same original wild stock, there is a vast difference among many of the varieties. In fact, pigeons have been produced in a wider selection of colors and varieties than any other domesticated bird or animal. That is one reason for their fascination.

Here are some of the more important and popular varieties, discussed in alphabetical order.

ANTWERP

This forerunner of the modern Racing Homer was developed from stock imported into England from Belgium between 1850 and 1860. Many birds came from around the city of Antwerp and thus the breed was given its name.

Antwerps are classified as short-, medium- or long-faced according to the length of the head from the center of the eye to the top of the upper mandible of the beak. The short-faced should measure 1⅜ inches.

The Antwerp is a large pigeon. The body is shapely, with a broad breast and deep chest. The back is long and straight, the shoulders broad. The tail feathers are short and carried so as not to touch the ground; the flight feathers are short, folded closely and resting on the tail.

Antwerps come in a wide variety of colors, with blood-red eyes. The beak is black, short and blunt. Legs are of medium length, with crimson feet.

Short-billed pigeons, as a rule, do not feed their young as well as the longer billed varieties. It is wise, therefore, to provide feeders of other breeds if you want to raise Antwerps in any quantity. (More about this in the chapter on breeding.)

ARCHANGEL

The origin of this small, racey, brilliantly colored pigeon is an unsolved mystery. There are numerous theories concerning the place of its beginning. Some authorities think the Archangel originated in Russia. Others say that it originated in Germany, while still others say that it is an Asiatic variety. The derivation of the name is just as obscure as the origin of the pigeon.

The Archangel is a delightful little pigeon and an excellent addition to any loft. Somewhat smaller than the common pigeon, it is alert in appearance. The Archangel is produced in a number of color varieties in Germany but only two, light bronze and dark bronze, have gained any popularity in the United States.

Both crested and uncrested varieties are bred. The Archangel stands erect and has a slender neck and body. Its outstanding characteristic is its lustrous plumage which has an almost metallic quality.

BARB

The Barb or Barbary Pigeon is one of the oldest breeds of domestic pigeon. It is the first type to be mentioned in English literature, with reference to the Barbary Pigeon appearing in Shakespeare's "As You Like It." It is thought that the Barb has changed little in appearance since that time.

It is probable that the Barb was first imported into continental Europe and England from Barbary in North Africa. This is by no means established fact, though, and the true origin of the Barb remains obscure.

The Barb is a medium-sized wattled pigeon with a large, broad and square head. It has a short, thick, slightly curved beak, a short neck and a long body. It stands erect. The cere, the naked circle of knobby flesh around the eyes, is coral red. The eyes themselves are white with a black pupil. Barbs are bred in black, dun, red, yellow and white.

CARNEAU

The Carneau, one of the most popular utility pigeons, originated along the border region of Southern Belgium and Northern France. It was brought to the United States in the early 1900's and today is found in almost every commercial loft of any size.

In addition to its function as a utility bird, it has made a place for itself as a show bird and is quite popular in that role. There is usually a large Carneau section in most of the larger pigeon shows. The first official show standard for Carneaux in the United States was drawn up and published in 1910.

The Carneau is a short, compact, heavy-set, broad-breasted

pigeon weighing from 22 to 26 ounces. The head is large, round and prominent. The large eyes are surrounded by a smooth, flesh-colored or red well-proportioned cere. The beak is of medium length and stout, with a smooth V-shaped wattle. The wings and tail are not too long. The flights are carried over the tail feathers, and the plumage is close fitting. Carneaux are bred in red, yellow, white, black and dun color.

The white Fantail rarely flies at all, but its beauty and breeding ability make it very popular.

This West of England Tumbler is known for its bald head and beautiful "boots."

CARRIER

The Carrier, often called the English Carrier, has long been bred in England where it has been a great favorite. Indeed, it was for a time known as the "King of Pigeons." There does not seem to be any record of when it was first brought to the United States, but it was exhibited in a pigeon show as early as 1873. It is thought that the Carrier originally came from Bazora in Persia.

As its name indicates, this pigeon was originally used to carry messages and was bred and kept for its homing ability. It has long since ceased to be used in this capacity and is now strictly a fancy variety. The Racing Homer far surpasses any homing or flying ability that the Carrier ever had. However, people still confuse a Homer with a Carrier. Whenever anyone speaks of a Carrier flying in a race or carrying a message, it is safe to assume that a Racing Homer is meant.

The main characteristics of the Carrier are the large body size, the enormous wattles around the beak and the hard, close-fitting plumage.

The Carrier is an extremely tall pigeon, measuring 17½ to 18½ inches. It is bred in black, dun, blue, red, yellow and white.

The beak wattle is snow white and the size of a walnut, rounded at the top and extending equally on each side of the beak. The lower part of the wattle, sometimes called the jewing, is similar to the upper so that together they have a rounded shape. The wattle usually does not attain its full growth until the pigeon is 3 or 4 years old. The eye wattle or cere is circular and about the size of a quarter.

CUMULET

The Cumulet, the French high-flying tumbler, is one of the ancestors of the Racing Homer. It is a medium-sized pigeon with a full chest and well-proportioned body. Its wings are long and powerful and its legs are fairly short. The Cumulet is usually pure white, but many specimens are flecked with red on the head and neck. This pigeon has never attained popularity in the United States.

DRAGOON

The Dragoon, of English origin, was probably bred directly from a now extinct pigeon called the Horseman. Some authorities believe that the Dragoon originated as a cross between the

Horseman and Tumbler. For a time the bird's name was spelled "Dragon," but "Dragoon" is more common today.

The Dragoon's distinctive characteristic is its wedge-shaped head. The short and blunt beak is carried parallel to the ground. The wattle on the beak is peg-shaped. The cere surrounding the eye is small and flesh-colored in white, red or yellow birds, and a dark reddish-purple in blues, silvers, checkers and grizzles.

The Dragoon has an erect, poised, rather wedge-shaped body, a short thick neck and short legs. It is a heavy bird, weighing 18 to 20 ounces. Once used as a utility bird, it has been largely replaced by Carneaux or Kings.

FANTAIL

One of the oldest, most popular and most familiar varieties, the Fantail originated in India. Also known as the broad-tailed shaker, it has been developed to its present state of excellence by English, Scotch and American breeders.

The Fantail is familiar to all. Its outstanding characteristic is its large fan-shaped tail. It has a small head and a slender neck which twitches as the bird struts or dances about on tiptoe. Its

White Fantails are most common, but this variety is bred in many other colors.

body is small but well rounded, and the chest is carried upright so that it is higher than the bird's head, which rests back on the cushion formed by the tail feathers. The legs are straight and fairly short. White is probably the most popular color, but Fantails are also bred in black, blue, red, yellow, silver, dun, checker and saddle. There is a lace or silky variety of Fantail, but it has gained little popularity in the United States.

For all its dainty appearance, the Fantail is reasonably hardy and a prolific breeder. The tail feathers should usually be cut during the breeding season as they tend to inhibit the mating activities of the birds. Fantails do not make the best parents, so it is often necessary to give their young to feeders or foster parents to be raised. Nevertheless, the Fantail is one of the most beautiful pigeons and is worthy of the time, effort and skill of any fancier.

Here a black Fantail struts about with his head held back.

This beautiful Short-Faced Tumbler is copper-colored. Although Tumblers were originally developed as flying pigeons that could perform aerial somersaults from great heights, today they are primarily show birds.

FLORENTINE

The Florentine, as the name implies, originated in Florence, Italy. It is one of the so-called hen pigeons, because its shape is similar to a hen's. Although it has been quite popular in some European countries and seems to be an ideal bird from the standpoint of good show material and good utility stock, it has never been very popular in the United States.

The Florentine is striking in appearance. It is a large pigeon, with colored head, colored wing coverts and tail. The rest of the plumage, including the flight feathers in the wings, is white. The Florentine has been bred in black, red, yellow, blue with black bars, blue checkered, brown with bars and various mottles and pieds.

HOMER

There are several varieties of Homers, all derived either directly or indirectly from the Racing Homer. They are:

Exhibition Homer. The Exhibition Homer was developed around 1900 and was probably bred from the Show Homer. It originated in England and has never been too popular in the United States. It is somewhat lighter in weight than the Show Homer and has a straight stout beak instead of the "Roman nose."

Genuine Homer. This variety was developed comparatively recently in England from the Racing Homer. Actually it is nothing more nor less than the exhibition counterpart of the Racing Homer. It has never attained much popularity here.

German Beauty Homer. Also bred from the Racing Homer, the German Beauty has been developed in Germany since 1907. It is an exhibition bird that closely resembles the Racing Homer except that it is somewhat thinner and more graceful. Recently introduced into the United States, it seems to be increasing in popularity.

Giant Homer. This variety was developed in the United States by breeding Racing Homers for size and squab-producing ability rather than for speed and homing instinct. A Giant Homer association was organized in 1928 and an official show standard has been set up. The Giant Homer is a good utility pigeon, but its main drawback is that some of the squabs are dark-skinned and therefore unmarketable. It is bred in a variety of colors, with silvers and blue checks the most popular.

Racing Homer. Although pigeons have been used for cen-

A pair of Racing Homers have begun a new nest while a youngster from their first round is still in the nest box. Youngsters should be removed from the nest box as soon as they are feathered. This is not only to protect the new eggs, but also because a squab will be severely pecked if it goes near newly-laid eggs!

turies as message-carriers, today's Racing Homer is a fairly recent breed developed in Belgium and England. This bird is the result of interbreeding the best flyers of several other breeds. In creating the Racing Homer, performance was the most important thing, with type, color and size of little concern.

In the days before modern means of communication or transportation the pigeon played an important part in carrying messages. It thus made possible and expedited trade and commerce between towns and cities that were some distance apart. In parts of Europe almost all merchants kept pigeons and sent them to correspondents in other trade centers, where the birds would

Racing Homers are sleek, streamlined birds with strong wings, deep chest and long tail.

A Danish Roller might be mistaken for a Racing Homer, except that its face is shorter and more pointed. Another difference is its eyes— small and light while a Homer's eyes are large and dark red.

be given messages to return to their owners. The homing pigeons were developed for their homing instinct and their speed of flying, and from them the Racing Homer was developed.

The part played by the homing pigeon in World War I, and, to a lesser extent, in World War II is common knowledge. Countless lives were saved and battles won because of messages carried by Racing Homers. It has been found that when other means of communication fail, pigeons are usually dependable. When all telephone lines were destroyed during a battle, pigeons were often the only means of communication between an isolated unit and the home base. The brave little birds saved the day on more than one occasion.

One pigeon, "Big Tom," was released at Grand Pre with an important message. He flew to his home loft 40 kilometers away in 25 minutes and when the message was taken from him it was found that one leg had been shot to pieces and there was a hole in his breast made by a machine gun bullet.

Another famous World War I bird was "Mocker," who carried an important message giving the location of several enemy batteries that were taking a heavy toll among the American forces. Even though he lost an eye en route, he delivered the message, and within 20 minutes of his arrival the batteries were silenced. "Mocker" died at Fort Monmouth, New Jersey, at the age of 20. The last of the World War I pigeon heroes to die, he was buried with military honors.

It is difficult to give an accurate description of a good Racing Homer since the birds vary somewhat in appearance. Like good race horses, they are not always the most beautiful of their species. A good racer is a sleek, streamlined bird with strong, muscular wings and a deep chest. The flight feathers should be well formed, broad and resilient. The tail should be fairly long, the head broad, the eyes bright and clear. Racing Homers come in a variety of colors.

Chapter 8 discusses the special problems of raising and training homing pigeons.

Show Homer. A product of England, the Show Homer was

developed from the Flying Belgium Antwerp pigeons in an effort to improve the exhibition qualities of that breed. It is a large pigeon, distinguished by its head which forms a long unbroken, well-arched curve from the tip of the beak to the back of the head. It is sometimes said to have a "Roman nose." Show Homers are bred in a variety of colors.

HUNGARIAN

Although the name implies that the Hungarian pigeon originated in Hungary, some authorities believe that its beginnings

Hungarian pigeons are distinguished by the white stripe that goes over the head and down the back. The marking is clearly visible on the top bird.

(Above) The Capped or Crested Mucky is an attractive pigeon. (Below) This Full-Headed Swallow shows the distinguishing colored "cap" and long foot feathers.

(Above) The Birmingham Roller has highly developed tumbling ability.
(Below) A blue-barred Pouter Pigeon is in its usual "look-at-me" pose.

were in nearby Austria instead. In any case, the birds were probably developed by crossing the Florentine, the Swallow and another pigeon that was brought in by the Turks who at one time occupied that part of Europe.

The Hungarian is a large, handsome hen-type pigeon. In Europe it has been used extensively as a utility pigeon, but in the United States it has never caught on for that purpose because of the yellow skin and flesh of the squabs. The larger American markets demand white-skinned squabs.

The unusual and striking markings of the Hungarian make it an excellent and popular fancy show pigeon. Its most distinguishing characteristic is the white stripe that arises at the base of the beak and runs over the head and down the back of the neck, widening to a large "V" and running down the side of the breast to the wing butts. Hungarians are bred in a variety of colors, including black, blue barred, blue checked, yellow, red, silver and dun.

ICE PIGEON

This pigeon, a member of the group of pigeons known as German Toys, derived its name from its light blue ice-like color. There are two main types, classified as clean-legged and muffed (with feathers on legs and feet). All are about the same color, but some have black or white bars while others are barless, and some are laced or checkered in white. Ice Pigeons have never been very popular in the United States.

JACOBIN

The Jacobin is one of the oldest breeds of domestic pigeons. Indeed, it is so old that accurate knowledge of its origin has long since been lost. It has been said that the Jacobin originated in Cyprus, but this, though probable, is by no means established as fact.

The pigeon is so named because the hood of feathers enveloping the back and sides of its head resembles the hoods worn by the Jacobin order of monks. The pigeon's hood is accompanied by a "chain" which is a continuation of it that runs down each side of the neck until it meets the "rose," a round spot between the shoulders. The mane grows from the point where neck and shoulders join and runs upward to meet the hood. Jacobins are bred in white, black, blue, silver, red and yellow.

Jacobins had for a long time been regarded as delicate pigeons that should be bred only be experienced fanciers. Today this belief is no longer held and the bird is regarded as a good feeder and breeder. However, Jacobins do not see well and fly very little, and they are best kept in a small loft or pen to themselves.

KING

Probably the most popular pigeon in America today, both for showing and for squab production, is the King. It is bred in white, silver, blue, red, yellow and dun, with the white and silver by far the most popular for both utility and show pur-

King pigeons are among the favorite utility birds. The squabs are in great demand for the deluxe restaurant trade. Farmers often raise Kings with their other fowl.

Oriental Frills, first bred in Turkey, get their name from their frill of breast feathers. Their short faces are a handicap in feeding their young, and if foster parents aren't used the squabs often die of starvation.

Another member of the Tumbler family, the Muff Tumbler, has an outstanding pair of boots.

The Jacobin, one of the world's fanciest birds, is also one of the world's oldest domesticated pigeons. The luxurious feathers are difficult to keep clean and a show specimen must be constantly babied.

The Lahore or La Houre pigeon is grouse-legged but does not have the elaborate boots of the Muff Tumbler. Its distinguishing characteristic is its white underparts. Some countries call it the Shirazi pigeon.

poses. The King is a pigeon of purely American origin. The White King is the result of crossing such pigeons as the Swiss Mondaine, Dragoon, Duchess and Florentine. The Silver King, first bred by C. Ray King of California, is a cross of Homer, Runt, Maltese and Mondaine.

The King is a medium-sized pigeon weighing between 26 and 35 ounces. It is solid and chunky in build, with a large, well-rounded head. The eyes are round and prominent, with eye color varying with the color of the birds. The cere and legs are bright red.

As a utility pigeon the King is unsurpassed. It is tame and prolific, and consistently produces white-skinned squabs of approximately one pound in weight, making it ideally suited to the commercial squab market.

LAHORE

Anglo-American fanciers call this pigeon after the Pakistani city of Lahore. Throughout Pakistan, India and Iran, however, the bird's name is "Shirazi," which means "coming from Shiraz" (a city in Iran where the breed probably originated). This pigeon's distinguishing characteristic is its white underparts—throat, chest, breast, abdomen and tail—and its colored head, back and wings. The Lahore is grouse-legged—it has feathers on its legs and feet. It is a fairly large bird and has occasionally been used as a utility breed, but its squabs are not large enough to compete with commercial breeds on the open market.

LARK

The Lark derives its name from the "larking" or triangular marks on its wing feathers, which resemble the markings of the European field lark. There are two varieties of Larks, the Coburg Lark and the Nuremberg Lark, both products of Germany.

The Coburg Lark is a large pigeon, broad breasted and long bodied, that is often used for utility purposes in Germany. The Nuremberg Lark closely resembles it, but is much smaller. Neither has ever been popular in America.

MAGPIE

The Magpie, originally one of the German Toys but now in a class by itself, is a small, graceful, streamlined pigeon. Its shallow body, long, tapering, snakey neck and small head give it the appearance of thinness. Its characteristic markings consist of white body, wings, shoulders and legs; colored head, neck, chest, back, rump and tail. Magpies are bred in black, blue, silver, red, yellow, cream and dun.

MALTESE

Today's Maltese, one of the group of hen pigeons, is of German or Austrian descent. It is a large bird, standing 15 inches or more in height. It was once used as a utility pigeon but is now bred almost exclusively as a show bird. The Maltese has a boat- or hen-shaped body and an extremely long neck. Its legs are long and straight and its tail feathers are straight and elevated so that the end of the tail is almost on a level with the back of the head. The Maltese is bred in black, blue, silver, white, red, yellow, and dun.

MODENA

The Modena, one of the prettiest and most popular show pigeons, originated as a flying pigeon in the Italian city it is named for. It was bred in Modena as early as the 14th century for the purpose of engaging in pigeon-flying, a sport peculiar to that city. Pigeon fanciers would turn out their flying kits or flocks of pigeons for the sole purpose of enticing birds from the kits of other fanciers. The birds were then either redeemed by their owner or kept by the owner of the loft to which they had been enticed. Often, where there was bitter rivalry, any pigeon captured from another loft was immediately killed and then hung where its owner would be sure to see it. A modified form of this "sport" still exists in Modena today.

The pigeon on the left is an English Turbit; its companion, a Bald-Headed Tumbler.

A white Dutch Frillback is not often seen.

The Modena is bred in two basic color patterns and in about 150 different colors. The *Gazzi Modena* is marked much like the Magpie with colored head, wings and tail and white body. The *Schietti Modena* is a plain-colored bird without the white markings of the Gazzi. Both types are small pigeons, about 10 inches in length, with a heavy-set or "cobby" but graceful appearance. The Modena is a good breeder.

MONDAINE

The Mondaine, which descended from field pigeons of France and Italy, comes in several varieties. The White Swiss Mondaine is most popular in America. It is an excellent utility pigeon, the equal of the King and Carneau in most respects. It is a long bird with a broad back and a long breast. The squabs frequently weigh more than a pound apiece. It is said that Mondaines do not produce quite as many squabs per year as some other commercial breeds, but production capacity seems to differ among the strains within each breed.

Besides being excellent utility pigeons, Mondaines make good show birds. Show standards have been set up for them and large classes are exhibited in the majority of pigeon and poultry shows held in the United States.

The French Gros Mondaine and the Indian Mondaine are also bred in some sections.

NUN

The Nun is one of the most attractive and at the same time one of the easiest fancy pigeons to breed and care for. First bred in Germany, it has been quite popular there and in other parts of Europe for several centuries. It was introduced into the United States at an early date.

The shell crest and characteristic markings of the Nun make it attractive and easily distinguishable from other breeds of pigeons. It is white, with colored head, bib, flight feathers and tail. The best looking specimens are marked in black, but Nuns are bred in other colors as well. It is a small, well-built, compact pigeon.

The Nun is friendly and easily tamed. It is not uncommon for Nuns to become so attached to their owner that they will fly to him whenever he comes into the loft. They do not have to be cooped up but may be allowed to come and go as they please.

ORIENTAL FRILL

The Oriental Frill, among the most beautiful and exotic of domestic pigeons, originated in Turkey. From there the bird was imported into continental Europe, Britain and the United States during the last century.

There are a number of color varieties. The most popular and important is the Satinette, which includes the Sulpherettes, Brunettes, Bluettes and Silverettes. Other Oriental Frills are Blondinettes, Turbiteens and Oriental Turbits.

All Oriental Frills have a frill of feathers on the breast. The majority are grouse-legged (with feathers on the legs and feet). They have short thick beaks and peaked crests which rise to a needle point above the highest point of the head. They are plump, round-bodied pigeons, somewhat smaller than the English Owls.

Satinettes have white bodies, with tri-colored markings of black, blue and dun on shoulders, wings, coverts and tail. The flights are white. The sub-varieties of the Satinette differ only in the colors of their markings.

Blondinettes have blue bodies, but are otherwise marked like Satinettes. (Some Blondinettes come in other colors.)

Turbiteens are white pigeons with colored wing coverts and colored spots below each eye and on the forehead.

Oriental Turbits differ from most of the other Oriental Frills in that they are clean-legged and plain-headed. They are white, with colored tail and wing coverts.

Like most short-beaked varieties, Oriental Frills do not make very good parents. It is therefore necessary to use foster parents of a long-billed variety as feeders.

Oriental Frills are easily tamed and become quite attached to their keeper. Because of their small size, they are easily kept and adjust nicely to small quarters when necessary.

OWL

The Owl is characterized by a short beak which, with the wattle and the rounded skull, forms a complete circle. There are several varieties, with the African, English and Chinese Owl most important and popular in the United States. The main difference between the African and English Owl is size; the African is the smallest domestic pigeon bred today.

The exact origin of the Owl is somewhat clouded, but it is probable that the pigeon originated in Asia or Asia Minor. English Owls have long been bred in England, but African Owls created quite a stir when they were first introduced into England from Tunis in 1858. They were imported in large numbers the following year.

Owls have clean legs, plain heads, and frills of feathers on the breast much like Oriental Frills and Turbits. English and African Owls are bred in black, blue, silver, white, red, yellow and dun. They are also poor parents, and feeders are required.

The *Chinese Owl* is of an intermediate size between the African and English. It resembles the other Owls except for its "whiskers," a frill of feathers that extends across the entire breast and runs up each side of the neck to meet in the back of the head. It also has a leg frill that grows from each leg and lies close to the body. Colors are black, blue, silver, red and yellow. The Chinese Owl has a longer beak than the African and English Owls and is therefore a better feeder.

POUTER AND CROPPER

The Pouter and Cropper are close kin, and together they make up a large family. Since they are all similar, a description of representative members of the family should suffice.

English Pouter. This is a very distinctive bird, not easily confused with other varieties. It has a large crop or globe, erect stature, slim waist and long legs. One of the tallest of all pigeons, it measures some 16 inches from head to toe. On its globe the English Pouter has a white crescent or half moon, with the ends extending to just beneath the eyes on both sides. Wing primaries, underside, and leg and feet feathers are white, and a group of white feathers on the wings forms the shape of a rose. The bird is bred in white, black, blue, red and yellow.

The origin of the English Pouter is somewhat obscure. Of unknown ancestry, it was probably bred from the Runt crossed with the Dutch Cropper.

Pouters are easily tamed. They are among the most amusing of all pigeons because they love to strut back and forth and get all the attention they can. This makes them particularly popular at pigeon shows where they always attract a great deal of attention.

Their vanity also accounts for the fact that they are indifferent breeders, for they are always more interested in strutting than in sitting on eggs or feeding young.

Pigmy Pouter. This bird is much like the English Pouter except for its smaller size, about 11 inches in height. It is quite playful and becomes attached to its keeper. Also fond of strutting, it is a much better parent than the English Pouter, and no foster parents or feeders are needed. The Pigmy's small size means that it requires only a small loft and less food than other varieties.

Dutch Cropper or *Old Holland Pouter.* This long-legged bird is among the oldest of Pouters, and is thought by many authorities to be *the* oldest. It is similar in appearance to the English Pouter but considerably stockier. Its legs and feet are muffed.

Old German Cropper. This type is distinguished from the Dutch Cropper by its clean short legs and extremely long wings. Its globe is more pear-shaped than round because of its carriage and short legs.

Brunner Pouter. This small Pouter resembles the English and

English Pouters are not good parents, for their vanity
makes them neglect their young.

Pigmy. It is bred in uniform colors of black, blue, white, red
and yellow and in white with black, red and yellow crowns. Its
origin is unknown.

Holle Cropper. Body shape and structure are much like the
Fantail, but the Holle Cropper does not have the fan-shaped tail.
Its head is held back so that the top of the globe is the highest
part of the body. The bird is bred in many colors and in uniform
black and white. The markings of the colored birds resemble
those of the English Pouter.

RUNT

The Runt, sometimes called the Giant Runt, is paradoxica.
the largest of the domestic pigeons. Good specimens weigh ...
pounds, and an occasional outstanding bird weighs 3½ pounds
or more. Its great size and weight make the Runt an excellent
utility pigeon, but it is not favored in the commercial squab
market because the squabs weigh considerably more than the
preferred pound. Although many Runt strains are not as prolific
as other utility breeds, there are some good strains that will
produce as many squabs as any other breed.

The Runt is one of the oldest of domestic pigeons. Although
its exact origin is unknown, it is mentioned in the earliest literature on pigeons. It is often referred to as the "Roman pigeon"
in European writings.

The Runt is often bred in coops, a pair to each coop, instead
of in a loft with a flight pen as are other utility breeds. Because
of their large size the birds do not fly much and need very little
flight exercise. Each coop should be about 6 feet wide by 7 feet
long by 6 feet high. The Runt's nest box should be at least 15
inches square, with plenty of nesting material.

Colors are black, blue, silver, white, red and yellow.

SCANDAROON

The Scandaroon somewhat resembles the Carrier in size,
shape and bearing. It has a longer, more curved beak than any
other member of the pigeon family. Its markings are similar to
the Magpie; its colors are black, blue, white, red and yellow.

The Scandaroon originated in Baghdad and was then brought
to Germany. It has never been popular in the United States.

STRASSER

The Strasser was developed in Austria as a utility pigeon,
but it cannot compete in the American market against the larger,

more prolific breeds such as the King and Carneau. However, it is quite popular as a fancy breed.

The Strasser is marked similarly to the Gazzi Modena. It has a colored head, neck, wings and tail, but it also has colored feathers on the back where the Modena does not have them. The rest of the body is white. Colors include blue, blue barred, black or white barred, blue checkered, red, yellow, black laced and lark colors.

SWALLOW

The Swallow is one of the most popular and attractive of the German Toys. Its body structure is similar to that of a field pigeon, with its chief distinguishing characteristic the shell crest and colored head or "cap." Some sub-varieties are clean-legged, but the most popular Swallows have long foot feathers or "boots."

There are a number of sub-varieties popular in Europe, but few of them are distinguished from one another in America. Swallows are bred in a variety of colors, including black, blue, silver, red and yellow.

TUMBLER

Tumblers make up one of the oldest and largest families of domestic pigeons. Popular for a long time, a number of varieties have been developed in various parts of Europe. Some types have been bred for show purposes; others, including the Rollers and Tipplers, have been bred for their flying ability and performance. Several of the more typical family representatives are:

English Short-Faced Tumbler. Like other Tumblers, this bird was developed as a flying pigeon with the ability to fly to great heights and then tumble to a lower level in a series of aerial somersaults. Now, however, it is bred primarily for show purposes and has virtually lost its flying and tumbling ability.

This Tumbler is a small, compact bird with a thin neck and

a large, powerful chest. Its two distinguishing characteristics are drooping flight feathers that fall below the level of the tail and the protruding frontal part of the skull that forms a knob as it rises straight up from the short beak.

Short-Faced Tumblers are bred in a number of different colors, with a wide variety of markings which include almond, baldhead and beard, mottled, agate and kite.

Long-Faced Tumbler. Both clean-legged and muffed varieties come in many colors. The Long-Faced Tumbler has a medium long face with a stout beak and a large round head about the size of a half dollar. Its body is short and thick-set, and its short neck is much thicker than that of the Short-Faced Tumbler. The flights are carried so they fold over the tail.

A wide variety of colors and markings exist.

Birmingham Roller. This bird was bred as a flying pigeon in Birmingham, England, and its tumbling or rolling ability was highly developed so that it can tumble or spin in a lightning-fast series of backward somersaults from a great height until considerable altitude is lost. In some places fanciers hold competitions to see whose pigeons are the best performers. Birmingham Rollers are also popular as fancy pigeons and exhibition birds, with a show standard set up for them.

Flying Tippler. Sustained flight is the most important attribute of this bird, which was developed from the Flying Tumbler. The ability to tumble has been bred out of the Tipplers and spending long hours in the air has been emphasized instead. Good specimens have been known to stay up more than 19 hours at a stretch.

In appearance the Tippler resembles the other members of the Tumbler family. Show standards were set up some years ago.

Parlor Tumbler (Ground or House Tumbler). This too is a typical Tumbler in body formation. The Parlor Tumbler is bred for its ability to jump into the air, turn one or more backward somersaults and land on its feet near its starting point.

German Tumbler. This type is divided into short-, medium- and long-faced varieties which come in many colors and combinations and both crested and plain-headed. Most of them have never achieved much popularity in the United States.

TURBIT

The Turbit, one of the most beautiful pigeons, is quite hardy and easily cared for. Its body is white, as are the flights, and the wing feathers are colored blue, black, red, yellow or dun. The Turbit somewhat resembles the African Owl. It has a frill on its breast, a crest that rises to a peak at the back of its head, clean legs and an extremely short beak, making it necessary to use foster parents when breeding.

Neither the exact age nor the origin of the Turbit is known. There are early references to it in the literature of England, France and Germany. It is quite popular in the United States.

4. Housing for Your Pigeons

The housing you provide for your pigeons depends somewhat on the type and number of pigeons you have and on your reasons for keeping them. What is ideal housing for fancy show birds is not always best for keeping and breeding Racing Homers or for producing squabs for market. Obviously pigeons that are to be kept closely confined and bred for show purposes will have housing requirements that are slightly different from those birds that are allowed to fly at liberty part or all of the time.

In general, pigeons are hardy, adaptable birds that thrive under a wide variety of conditions. You may provide them with a loft or dovecote (an outdoor pigeon house containing nesting accommodations for a number of pairs) and allow them liberty to come and go as they please. Or you may keep them in a loft with flight pens attached so that they can get a certain amount of exercise. A third possibility is keeping them in small cages, where they seem to thrive.

There are three things you should keep in mind when you plan the housing facilities for your pigeons. You must consider their comfort first, then your own convenience as far as caring for them and cleaning is concerned, and the cost of building and maintaining the facilities.

It is not difficult to keep your birds comfortable. Whatever quarters you provide should be airy and well ventilated but not drafty — there should be plenty of fresh air available but the birds should be able to get out of drafts when they wish. Nor should they be deprived of sunlight, since they need its warm, health-giving rays if they are to thrive.

The quarters should be dry. Pigeons do not mind cold

This modest loft was made from scrap material and added on to an old garage. Pigeons are not choosy about their home, but it is very hard to keep an old coop clean.

weather as long as it is not too extreme or sustained, but they cannot tolerate dampness.

And again, for your convenience, the pigeons' housing should be built so that you can clean easily. See page 19 for information about cleaning. Chapter 8 discusses the special housing required for Racing Homers.

LOFT SIZE

The size of your loft depends on the type and number of pigeons you intend to keep. However, it is a good idea to start out with space available for considerably more pigeons than you start with or intend to obtain in the foreseeable future. A pigeon flock has a way of increasing more rapidly than its owner expects and often a fancier suddenly realizes that he has too many pigeons for his space. He is then faced with the choice of either disposing of some of his pigeons or going to the trouble and expense of constructing additional housing facilities. Of course

This coop is on top of the building where this book was printed. It was built from scrap lumber and cost less than $50. For some really fancy pigeon lofts, see pages 102 to 107.

If you are just interested in keeping a few pigeons, they can share a large flight with other birds. Unless strange birds try to invade the privacy of their nest, pigeons get along well with others.

All kinds of pigeons can be kept together, as you see here. The only problem with keeping different varieties together is that they will interbreed and worthless mixes will result. The trade call these mixes "rats."

there has to be a stopping place somewhere, but when you first begin building it is little more expense or trouble to provide some extra space for the future.

Before you build your loft, therefore, estimate the number of pigeons you would eventually like to keep, and plan with that number in mind. Then, to determine the size your loft should be, allow for a square of floor space that measures 18 inches on each of the sides for each pair of large fancy or utility breeds. (Note that this dimension is not square inches, but 18 inches on all four sides.)

A loft that will comfortably accommodate 18 to 25 pairs of pigeons, depending on breed and size, can be constructed according to the following dimensions. The loft itself should be

8 to 10 feet wide, 6 to 8 feet high, and about 12 feet deep. A flight pen the same width and height as the house should project from it. This should be another 10 to 12 feet in depth. (If the loft or flight pen is much higher than the recommended 6 to 8 feet, you will be unable to tame your pigeons as readily and it will be more difficult to catch them when necessary.)

If you live in a mild climate you will not have to enclose the front of the loft. Pigeons can stand a reasonable amount of cold, but if you live where the winters are severe it is best to enclose the loft, leaving windows in front that can be opened in mild weather so the birds can go back and forth to the flight pen.

FLIGHT PEN

Cover the flight pen with 1-inch mesh poultry wire. While larger mesh is satisfactory for keeping the pigeons in, it also allows sparrows and other small birds to enter. They can eat a lot of feed and make a nuisance of themselves. One-inch mesh will keep most of them out. There is no need to use hardware cloth or other small meshed wires, since any advantage it may have (and it is debatable that it has any) is not worth the additional expense.

USING EXISTING FACILITIES

Everything said thus far assumes that you will be building a loft especially for your pigeons. Actually this is not at all necessary. Probably most pigeon fanciers do not build a special loft, to begin with anyway, but use the facilities offered by an already existing building. A pigeon loft may be in a barn, garage, chicken house, attic or any other building that will suit your pigeons' needs. One pigeon owner uses a small space in an old building that was once a college dormitory but is now used as a warehouse. He has a well-cared-for flock of Kings and Racing Homers too.

If you use an existing building as your loft, you can build

This inside view of the TFH pigeon loft shows the nest boxes.

an outdoor flight just as you would if you were constructing a new loft from start to finish. If this is not practical, you can provide flight space inside the loft itself.

If you are keeping Racing Homers or another type of pigeon bred and kept for its flying ability, it is best to have your loft above ground level. An attic, garage roof or barn loft is ideal. The fact that it is easy to spot and reach could make the difference between winning and losing races.

NEST BOXES

The size of the nest boxes also depends to a great extent on the kind and size of pigeons you keep. Obviously what would be adequate for a pair of African Owls would be far from adequate for a pair of Giant Runts. In general, however, one cubic foot of nesting space is enough for most types of pigeons. Some of the larger breeds will require a little more space.

You should provide two nesting boxes for each pair of pigeons, because they will often lay and start incubating a second clutch of eggs before their squabs are fully grown and ready to leave the first nest. The nest boxes should either have removable bottoms or nest bowls (available from your pet shop or pigeon supply dealer) placed in them. This makes cleaning easier. You should clean the boxes thoroughly after each pair of squabs is hatched, and you might clean even more often if you can do it without disturbing the eggs or squabs too much.

Even though they don't do it very well, pigeons do build nests, so you must provide nesting materials for them. Tobacco stems and pine straw are among the best materials as they give off an odor that keeps mites and other insect pests away. If you can't obtain either of these materials, you may use any type of straw, grass or twigs.

Put the nesting materials where the pigeons can get it and where they will not have too far to carry it to their nest boxes. Some fanciers put cedar sawdust, which acts as a deterrent to mites, in the bottom of the nest boxes and let the pigeons build their nests on top. Others omit the sawdust and dust a little mite powder directly into the bottom and crevices of the boxes. If you use both pine straw or tobacco stems and mite powder, you will have very little to worry about as far as mites are concerned.

PERCHES

The best perches for use in both the loft and the flight pen are either flat boards 2 inches or more in width or inverted V-shaped perches. The old ladder-type perches have never been satisfactory and are not recommended.

Place the perches in front of the nest boxes so that the cock bird can roost just outside the nest while the hen incubates the eggs at night. If you wish, you can place other perches in the flight, but don't put them under one another where they can get fouled by the droppings of pigeons sitting above. Don't put the perches too high either. You can more easily observe and catch your pigeons if the perches are below your eye level. A good height for perches in the flight pen is 4 feet.

Perches placed in convenient locations will provide additional comfort for your pigeons.

5. Feeding Your Pigeons

Providing well-balanced, proper feed for your pigeons is one of the most important elements in successful pigeon-keeping. Although pigeons may seem to get along pretty well on inferior feeds for a time, sooner or later they will become weak and subject to disease or dietary deficiency.

READY-MIXED FEEDS

Since there are several good commercial pigeon feeds on the market, there is no reason for not feeding well-balanced rations. Ready-mixed feeds consisting of top-quality grains of various kinds are readily obtainable through your local pet shop, feed store or pigeon supply dealer. If you prefer, you can probably save a little money by ordering from a wholesale supply house in one of the larger feed centers of the country.

PREPARING YOUR OWN FORMULA

The commercial mixtures are good and reasonable in price. Unless you have a vast number of pigeons in a squab-raising plant or some similar enterprise, there is little to be gained by buying the ingredients separately and mixing them yourself. But if you want to, of course you can.

There are probably almost as many formulas for pigeon feed mixtures as there are pigeon fanciers, and each fancier is sure that his formula is the very best. Actually many of them differ little as far as food value is concerned. A good basic formula

Different types of foods are available for different purposes. If you are raising pigeons for the market and you have large birds like this one to feed, you will not buy as expensive a feed as you would for Racing Homers or fancy birds.

that can be varied slightly one way or another consists of equal parts of corn (preferably yellow corn), field peas, hard red wheat, Kaffir corn or milo. You can vary and supplement this from time to time with such small grains as millet, rice, oats, barley, hemp and so forth.

No matter what formula you use, you must be sure that all grains are clean, dry and well-seasoned — grain that is not newly harvested but that has been allowed to dry and season thoroughly for several months. If you feed grain that is dirty, damp or mildewed you are asking for trouble.

It would be impossible to estimate how many wild pigeons, living in nearly every large city in the world, subsist and do well on a diet of bread crumbs. This photo was taken by Mr. Bengué, the drug manufacturer, who has made a habit of feeding wild pigeons at his window sill, both in New York and Paris.

PELLET FEED

Some very good prepared pellet pigeon feeds are on the market. They are properly balanced and made up of first-quality ingredients that have been ground and then pressed into pellet form. There is usually a little difficulty in getting pigeons started on this type of feed, since it is totally different from anything that instinct tells them is edible, but once they have been successfully introduced to it they seem to thrive.

Even if your pigeons eat from your hand, it is not good sense to disturb a hen sitting on her eggs. If she doesn't eat when the other birds do, she will see to it that she has her turn at the next feeding.

GREEN FOOD

Most authorities agree that pigeons should be fed a certain amount of green food in addition to their regular diet of grain. You do not have to give your pigeons green food every day; once a week should be enough. Since there are many satisfactory green foods readily obtainable — grass clippings, chickweed, lettuce, kale, celery tops and so forth — it is little extra trouble to add them to your pigeons' diet and perhaps improve their health and stamina as a result. If your pigeons are allowed their liberty, they will be able to obtain their own greens and you need not worry about it.

FEEDING METHODS

You have a choice of feeding methods as well as a choice of feeds. Most fanciers who have only a few pigeons prefer to feed their birds by hand twice a day, scattering grain on the floor of the loft or fly pen. Hand-feeding your pigeons will give you the chance to get better acquainted with them and to observe their health and physical condition. Hand-fed pigeons soon come to know their owners and tend to be much tamer than pigeons that are fed by other methods.

Scatter as much feed on the ground as your pigeons will eat in about 15 or 20 minutes. As time goes on and you get better acquainted with your birds and their habits, you will come to know when you have fed them enough. You will notice that they start to lose interest in their food and to be a bit more flighty as their appetites begin to be satisfied.

Feed your pigeons twice a day, in early morning and in midafternoon. It is far better to underfeed than to overfeed them. More pet birds are killed with kindness than are starved to death.

If you have a large number of pigeons — hundreds or thousands — or if you have to be away for considerable periods of time, hand-feeding will not be possible. Your best solution is to use feeders, keeping feed before your birds at all times. Or you may have the feeders filled from outside the pens or loft twice a day.

Using feeders has the advantage of being quick and easy, but it also has drawbacks. Feeders furnish a constant supply of food not only for your pigeons but for rats, mice and other pests as well. Then, too, there is the added problem of keeping both feed and feeders clean. This can develop into quite a task when you have many pigeons.

Many pigeon fanciers throw the seed on the ground and entice their flocks to come down to eat. With this method, a stray bird that has joined the flock can be easily trapped while on the ground.

If you have a large stock of birds, you can check their health by watching them when they eat. If you hand-feed your pigeons, you can get a really close view of them and thus observe any signs of diseases.

GRIT

In addition to food, pigeons need grit before them at all times. Grit serves two purposes. It acts as the pigeons' teeth, grinding up the food they eat. It also supplies the minerals needed to build bones, feathers, beaks and eggshells. *Grit is thus an absolute necessity.* Your pigeons can get along without it for *short* periods of time, but if they are deprived of it for very long they will sicken and die.

There are a number of good pigeon grits available through your feed, pet or pigeon supply dealer, but if you prefer you can obtain the ingredients separately and mix your own. A good

Racing Homers require a special diet, but the diet of every pigeon should include grit. This aids in digestion and is absolutely necessary for the health of your birds.

grit contains crushed rock (either granite or limestone), ground oyster shell, charcoal, salt, bone meal and trace minerals — minerals needed in minute quantities by the birds. A mixture of trace minerals is also available through your dealer. Keep a good grit mixture before your pigeons at all times, and make sure both the grit and its container are clean.

WATER

Your pigeons should have clean drinking water before them at all times. You can rig up some fountain arrangement so that they can drink from a drip or trickle of water. If you use water containers instead, clean them every day.

Keep the pigeons' bath and drinking water separate. As you learned in Chapter 2, the pigeons should be given the opportunity to bathe at least three times a week, and daily in warm weather. With frequent bathing your pigeons will keep themselves clean and healthy. Remember too that frequent bathing increases the hatchability of eggs by keeping the shells soft and pliable.

After the pigeons have completed their baths, empty the bath pans so that the birds cannot drink the bath water. Give them fresh water for each bath.

If you feed your pigeons well, provide them with good grit, and allow them to keep themselves clean, you should have a healthy, happy flock of birds.

6. Pigeon Breeding

How to distinguish between male and female pigeons was discussed on page 16. When you are ready to begin breeding your pigeons, you should be sure you have true pairs.

When pigeons are left to their own devices, and when they are in a wild state, they are monogamous and usually mate for life. Fortunately for the breeder of fancy show, racing or utility stock, a pigeon will readily accept a new mate if it is forcibly separated from its present mate and placed in a coop with the prospective one. But unless forcibly separated, a bird will adhere to its mate for life. Occasionally a bird that is cooped up with mated pairs will entice the mate of another bird, so it is not a good idea to keep single birds, either male or female, in the same loft or pen with mated birds.

In moderate climates pigeons will breed the year around, raising pair after pair of young. This, of course, is ideal for the commercial squab breeder whose stock has been developed to do just that, but the pigeon keeper who has valuable show or racing birds may want to hold his pigeons to 2 or 3 nests per year. This is best done by separating the sexes or withholding nesting facilities.

STANDARDS FOR CHOOSING MATES

The standards for choosing mates for your pigeons will vary considerably with each variety. Before you pair the birds, you should know what qualities are considered important in each

A female Racing Homer sits on her eggs. After a while the male will take his turn. Good birds should be limited to three nests per year.

breed and thus have some goal to aim for. Try to obtain birds that have as many of the good qualities of the variety as possible.

If you mate a bird that tends to be particularly strong in one quality with a bird that is weak in that quality, the young will probably be well-balanced. You may take into consideration more than one quality in this kind of mating.

In order to consistently produce birds with the characteristics you deem most important, you will want to develop your own strain or family of birds that have similar characteristics or a "family resemblance." To develop such a strain, you will have to use one or more of the systems of breeding referred to by geneticists and producers of outstanding livestock as inbreeding, line-breeding and outcrossing.

The mother and her youngsters are all differently colored and marked.

A pigeon egg is about half the size of a chicken egg.

INBREEDING

Inbreeding is the name for the breeding of closely related stock — father to daughter, mother to son, grandfather to granddaughter, grandmother to grandson, brother to sister, cousin to cousin. Inbreeding tends to accentuate the qualities of the parents (both good and bad) in the offspring. It tends to fix characteristics and reduce variation in the strain, and is particularly valuable in producing a strain of show or racing birds.

LINEBREEDING

Linebreeding, a form of inbreeding, is the system of breeding offspring back to one outstanding ancestor. Thus all birds of the strain are closely related to the ancestor and to each other.

OUTCROSSING

Outcrossing is breeding an unrelated bird into an inbred or linebred strain and thus introducing new blood. This may be desirable from time to time to prevent the accentuation of weaknesses due to too much inbreeding.

AGE FOR BREEDING

Although young pigeons are sexually mature and will breed when they are 4 to 6 months of age, they make the best breeders when they are between 1 and 3 years old. The productive life of the average pigeon varies. Some strains live longer and produce for a longer time than others. A good hen can normally produce satisfactorily for around 5 years, an exceptional one for 7 or 8 years. Cocks can generally be expected to live a little longer and breed a little longer than hens.

MATING COOP

If you are mating pigeons of your own choice (rather than the birds' choice) a good coop to use consists of two compartments separated by a removable wire partition. Place the pigeons in the coop, one in each compartment, where they can see but cannot get to each other. You will be able to keep breeding records easily if you make use of the numbered mating bands that slip on the pigeons' legs and can be removed at the end of the breeding season when the pairs are separated.

At first the two birds in the coop will probably ignore each other. After a while—it may be just a few hours or as long as

Mating coops have a temporary partition that can be removed when the birds show the desire to pair.

several days—the birds will begin to show some interest in each other and will show the desire to pair. When this occurs, remove the partition. Keep the birds in the mating coop for several days before returning them to the flight or giving them their liberty.

COURTSHIP

The courtship of pigeons is quite a colorful and fascinating ceremony. First the male pigeon directs his advances toward the hen of his choice. He struts and coos continually as he dances about the hen with crop inflated, body feathers ruffled, wing and tail feathers spread. He often attempts to press against the hen. If the hen is ready to mate, she shows her interest by bobbing her head and swallowing air so that her neck swells and pulsates visibly.

Billing follows mutual consent to mate. The female inserts her beak into that of the male, who feeds her small amounts of feed regurgitated from his crop. When billing occurs it is a sure sign that mating is soon to follow. Unmated pigeons do not bill.

Mating usually takes place shortly after billing. The birds take off on their nuptial flight over the loft or, if they are confined, they fly around and around the flight or cage.

The first egg is laid soon after the nest is finished, the second two days later.

NESTING

After mating, the cock pigeon chooses a nesting spot if he has not already done so. If your pigeons are confined, they will have the nest boxes you have provided; if they are in large lofts or allowed their liberty they may make their own choice.

Nest building usually begins within a week after the birds have mated and chosen the site. Most pigeons are poor nest builders—their nests are little more than a loosely constructed pile of twigs and straw. As you learned in Chapter 4, you should provide nest materials, preferably pine needles and tobacco stems, placed not too far from the nest boxes where the pigeons can find and carry them easily. The cock usually finds the materials and brings them, only one piece at a time, to the hen. She weaves them into the nest. During the nest building the hen does not gather any material but later, after the eggs are laid, she may occasionally bring a piece or two while the cock is incubating the eggs.

Between the time the nest is begun and the first egg is laid, the cock drives the hen unmercifully. He seems to be terribly jealous of her and does not give her a moment's peace. He follows her constantly from place to place, scarcely giving her time to eat or drink. This behavior stops when the first egg is laid.

BROODING

Pigeons lay two eggs per nest. The first egg is laid shortly after the nest is finished. It usually happens during late afternoon, and is white and smooth. The hen begins to brood or incubate this egg lightly.

Serious brooding does not begin until the hen lays the second egg, usually two days later. Both parents incubate the eggs, but the hen does the larger share of the task. She usually sits on the nest from about 4:00 o'clock in the afternoon until between 9:00 and 10:00 the next morning. Then the cock takes his

A normally friendly pigeon might stand up and slap your hand with its wing if you disturb it on the nest. The sting of a strong wing slap is moderate, but protect your eyes from a particularly vehement bird.

If you don't supply your birds with sufficient nesting materials, they will pick up feathers and bits of straw from the outside and construct their own nest.

turn. The eggs are never left alone for more than a few minutes at a time. If they are allowed to remain unattended for long, they will cool, the embryos inside the shells will die, and the eggs won't hatch when the time comes.

It usually takes 17 to 19 days for pigeon eggs to hatch, although the time varies somewhat, depending on the temperature. After a few days of incubation it is easy to tell whether the eggs are fertile. Infertile eggs remain white, while fertile eggs change to grayish-blue in color as the embryo develops in the shell.

Remember that the pigeons should be able to bathe frequently while they are incubating eggs. The moisture carried back to the nest on the feathers helps to make the eggshell soft and pliable so that the young pigeon inside will have no trouble cracking the shell when the time comes for it to emerge.

Sometimes a bird will scorn a nest box and raise young right on the floor. A hen that lays her eggs on the floor is usually a bad parent who abandons her young before too long.

THE SQUABS

Newly hatched squabs are surprisingly ugly and helpless creatures. It is hard to realize that within just a few weeks they will be fully grown, completely feathered pigeons.

When it emerges from the egg the squab is blind and so weak that it cannot hold its head up. Within a few hours, after the yolk sac is absorbed, the squab begins to raise its head and look for food. The parent bird that is on the nest, whichever one it happens to be, becomes aware of the baby's hunger and begins to feed it. This is a task that will be performed literally hundreds of times within the next few weeks.

These young Homers with full crops are almost ready to leave the nest. In about another week the squabs will be pushed out of the nest by their mother or father. The white tip on the bill and the soft yellow down visible on the full crop will soon disappear.

Squabs are fed by both parents. Even after they leave the nest box the youngsters will recognize their mother and father and follow after them with wings outstretched, screaming for food.

The squabs are fed by their parents on a white cheese-like substance formed in the parents' crops. This substance, called "pigeon milk," appears in the crops at just about the time the eggs hatch. The parents feed the squabs by regurgitation, pumping the food out of their own crops into those of the squabs. After about a week the squabs are fed less "pigeon milk" and more and more solid food, consisting of grains of various kinds, until finally they are fed entirely on solids.

For the first week the young pigeon can raise its head for food but does not seem to notice anything else. When the bird is a few days old you can put the seamless band on its leg. (See page 22.) At about the tenth day the pinfeathers begin to appear and the squab notices any intruder. Indeed, birds of this age will try to frighten away intruders by hissing and popping their beaks. Until the squab is about 3 weeks old, it is completely dependent on its parents for food and makes no effort to feed itself or to pick up grain. The squab that is able to ask louder for food is always fed first. Often, therefore, the squab that is hatched first is fed first and so develops more quickly than its nestmate. Sometimes one squab is so neglected and underfed that it dies, while its nestmate thrives. As the squabs grow older, their demands for food become more and more urgent, until finally they reach the age where they can fend for themselves—at about 4 or 5 weeks. By this time, too, they are fully feathered.

When feeding, the youngster shoves its beak deep into its parent's mouth and takes the regurgitated seed. Short-faced birds have trouble feeding their young.

This pair of squabs is about 10 days old.

Some squabs are very brave and aggressive. When you reach to touch them or pick them up they will rise up and peck at your hand.

Foster parents are often used to bring up the young of poor feeders.

FOSTER PARENTS

The use of foster parents as feeders was mentioned earlier. This is a common practice among breeders of fancy show or racing stock and is necessary for raising the young of poor feeders (see Chapter 3).

Foster parents are usually pigeons of one of the hardy long-billed varieties that are kept specifically for this purpose. They must have eggs or squabs at about the same stage of development as the eggs or young to be substituted. The foster parents' own eggs or young are sacrificed for the worthy cause of raising strong racing or show stock. If it is already-hatched squabs rather than eggs that are substituted, this must take place be-

With fancy birds that have very short faces like this Turbit, it may be necessary to remove the squabs as soon as they are born and hand-feed them.

fore the young feather out. If the foster parents recognize that the young are not their own, they will not accept or care for them, and may even kill them.

RAISING THE YOUNG

After the squabs leave the nest the cock will probably feed them for another week or 10 days. By this time the chances are that the hen is busy incubating another clutch of eggs in another nest, and before long the parents will begin the task of rearing two more squabs. (In a commercial squab plant, the young are killed for market before they leave the nest.)

When the young pigeons are 4 to 6 months of age they are sexually mature and ready to choose their own mates and begin the process of raising families themselves. For the production of sound, healthy birds for show and racing purposes, it is best to restrain them from pairing and breeding until they are at least a year old. Therefore you should separate the young birds from the older birds, as the older ones' presence will stimulate the young to pair off earlier.

If you are raising show or racing stock it is best to separate the pairs from about the middle of June until after the molt in the fall. That way the pigeons will not be raising and feeding young during the molt. Many authorities believe that it is detrimental both to the parents and the offspring if the parents care for young during the time when they are replacing their feathers. Other authorities say that as long as the parents are properly fed and cared for no harm will come from caring for young during the molt. The weight of evidence seems to be with the latter, since many commercial squab farms raise young pigeons in large numbers during every month of the year. However, it would probably be best to stop breeding activities in your loft during the summer and early fall, until you have become an experienced pigeon-raiser.

So that a female may be bred again soon, she is sometimes taken from her young and the male is allowed to raise them by himself.

Only healthy pigeons have any value. Sick birds are a liability. They cannot fly properly and their sense of direction and timing is poor. For the sake of your birds and your own investment, take care of them.

7. Keeping Your Pigeons Healthy

Most pigeons are healthy, hardy creatures that get along nicely with a minimum of care and attention. But of course they do require *some* care and attention if they are to remain in good condition. Like most birds and animals, they are susceptible to some illnesses and to accidents, but for the most part poor health can be prevented.

You already know that to keep your pigeons in good condition, you must (1) provide light, airy, dry quarters where your pigeons can get out of direct drafts and where they will be comfortable in all weather; (2) keep these quarters clean; (3) provide clean, well-seasoned food and make sure that the diet is well-balanced; (4) provide a well-balanced grit; (5) have plenty of clean drinking water available and separate water for frequent bathing.

If you follow these rules, you can keep most pigeon pests and diseases to a minimum. However, in spite of all the good care you provide, there will probably be an occasional outbreak of trouble of one type or another. You should be aware of several fairly common insect pests and pigeon ailments so you can be on the alert for them and take the necessary steps before they cause serious trouble.

INSECT PESTS

These are the common insect pests that infect pigeons:

Lice. By far the most common insect pests found on pigeons are one or another of the several varieties of pigeon lice. Although lice are very small, they are clearly visible to the naked eye, and if they are present you can see them when you examine your birds. They are not bloodsucking insects, but live off the feathers or skin scales. They spend their full life cycle on the pigeon's body, never leaving it. Unless lice are present in large numbers they are not much of a health hazard or nuisance. In warm weather they multiply rapidly. You can control or kill lice by using the insecticides and remedies for poultry lice that are available at poultry, feed, drug or pet stores. Sodium flouride is one of the cheapest and most effective remedies. In powder form, you can dust it under the pigeon's feathers. You may also use sodium flouride as a dip, mixing it in the proportion of 1 ounce to a gallon of water. A third way to apply it is to make a weaker solution—2 tablespoons to 4 gallons of water—and use it as the pigeon's bath water once every two weeks for three or four applications.

Red Mites. Red mites, or chicken mites, are quite different from lice and unfortunately they are harder to deal with if you have large numbers of pigeons. They infest the cracks and crevices of nest boxes and lofts and come out onto the pigeons only to feed, usually at night. When they are finished feeding (they are bloodsuckers) they return to the cracks and crevices. You will have to examine the loft and nests carefully to discover if mites are present. Tiny black pepper-like spots—actually dried blood—are a sign of mites.

There are a number of good mite powders available that can be dusted in the bottoms of nest boxes to help prevent or control an infestation. If you have only a few birds you can dust the powder under the feathers, but if you have many birds this will be impossible. You can also obtain effective insecticides to paint or spray into the crevices of your loft to eradicate red mites. Kerosene painted into the crevices of the loft and nest boxes is also a good remedy. An infestation of red mites can be a serious menace to squabs and older birds alike, so if you discover their presence you must act at once.

Pigeon Flies. These flies, somewhat smaller than houseflies, are found in lofts in the southern part of the United States.

They are not only a nuisance but can be disease-carriers. You can recognize the pigeon fly by its somewhat flat appearance and lively, quick movements. When it is disturbed it either flies away or buries itself under the feathers of the pigeon on which it is resting. The larvae, which resemble small lead shot, are deposited under the edges of the pigeon's nest, usually the nest containing squabs.

The best method of getting rid of the pigeon fly is to clean the nests regularly and thoroughly to destroy the larvae. Then spray the loft and birds to get rid of adult flies. There are several good sprays obtainable through your dealer.

There are other insect pests that you may come across from time to time, but lice, mites and flies are most common.

PIGEON DISEASES

There are several diseases and infections that you should know something about when you begin to keep and raise pigeons. They are as follows:

Canker. This protozoan infection is one of the most common of pigeon diseases. It usually occurs in squabs in the nest but adult birds may also have it. The symptom of canker is a lesion in the mouth or throat covered by a cheesy, yellowish-white substance. It continues to enlarge until it kills the bird. There are several effective remedies. One of the best is to swab the lesion with a solution made up of 3 parts glycerine and 1 part iodine. Although canker can be cured, if the infected birds are not particularly valuable it is best to do away with them so that the loft will not be contaminated. Some authorities say that canker is not contagious, but if it appears in the loft, isolate the affected birds and disinfect the entire loft with a hot lye solution.

Colds. Colds in pigeons are similar to colds in humans, and are probably due to the same causes. If you have a number of birds that are sick with colds, check your loft for dampness or

If a pigeon ever becomes ill and must be given liquid medicine, this is the proper way to administer it.

drafts. Improving conditions in the loft will often end your trouble with colds.

Pigeons seem to respond to the same cold treatments that humans do. Keep the ailing birds warm and give them cod liver oil to build up their strength. You may also give them castor oil to clean out their systems. Medicated salve or camphorated oil helps open the nostrils and makes breathing easier. There are a number of poultry and cage bird remedies containing sulpha drugs or antibiotics that give good results. These are available from your pet or poultry supply dealer. Colds will usually clear up of their own accord if the pigeon is kept warm and out of a draft.

Pneumonia. If the pigeon's throat is parched, it has some difficulty in breathing, appears to be feverish, and gives the appearance of being a very sick bird, it probably has pneumonia. Keep the bird warm and out of drafts. The best treatment is the use of sulpha and antibiotic drugs.

Roup. Roup occurs in pigeons most frequently in winter when the birds have been exposed to drafts or dampness. It is quite contagious. The symptoms are similar to a cold at first, but soon the nasal discharge changes from a watery mucus to a thick yellow, pus-like mucus which clogs the nostrils. One or both eyes may swell and finally completely close.

When you treat roup, isolate the ailing birds and thoroughly disinfect the loft and all utensils. Cover the loft floor with fresh sawdust and whitewash the loft itself. Then bathe the nostrils and eyes of the sick birds with a weak solution of boric acid or potassium permanganate. There are some remedies on the market that will help to clear up the roup without too much difficulty if you begin treatment in its early stages. Consult your dealer.

Diarrhea. In pigeons diarrhea is usually caused by eating unseasoned, moldy or sour grain. It will usually clear up after the cause is removed. The best remedy is to feed corn and small grains until the pigeon is better. It might be beneficial to give a dose of castor oil or Epsom salts to clear out the bird's system.

Egg Binding. Occasionally a hen will have trouble passing an egg. First of all, you should keep her warm. Bathe the vent with warm water and syringe a little warm olive oil into it. The hen will usually have no difficulty passing her egg after this treatment.

"Going Light." When a pigeon "goes light," the flesh wastes away and the bird takes on a sickly, emaciated appearance. Usually diarrhea is present too. "Going light" is not a disease itself, but a symptom of some other malady. Treating it is usually hopeless unless the real trouble can be found and treated. However, it helps to withhold all food until the crop is empty, and then feed the bird warm milk with bread or meal.

Again, pigeons that are housed in clean, dry, well-kept, draft-free lofts, that are properly fed, and allowed to keep themselves clean, are seldom sick. A word to the wise is sufficient.

A broken leg requires a splint, put on like this.

8. Training Your Pigeons

If you have decided that the pigeons for you are Racing Homers or any of the other flying varieties, such as Rollers, Tipplers or High Flyers, it will be necessary for you to train them to whatever type of performance they have been bred for.

Although it is instinct that causes Homers to return home and Rollers to go into their unique performance, the pigeons cannot be expected to develop the ability that has been bred into them without training and opportunity. Just as a thoroughbred horse must be trained before it can win races, so must a pigeon be trained to the performance that is expected of it.

Although there are some similarities in training Racing Homers for the race and in training other flying pigeons, there are even more differences. Let us look first at Racing Homers.

RACING HOMERS

First, a word of caution. In order to do a good job of training you must have something to work with. This means that you should have good stock. When you begin to raise Racing Homers, by all means get the best stock you can afford. Then do all you can to improve it by selective breeding and exceptionally good care. In most cases you will find it easier to train good stock, because the homing instinct is more pronounced in the birds and they have more stamina. On the other hand, one of the quickest routes to discouragement and failure is to get inferior stock.

You need something else, too, when you begin to raise and train Racing Homers—an abundance of patience. Without it, you are doomed to almost certain failure. With it, you can look forward to success.

Racing Homers do have much in common with other pigeons, but you will get best results in raising, training and racing them if you cater to their special needs. It is absolutely essential that Racing Homers are kept clean and free of mites and other pests. If they are to win races they must be kept in top physical condition with proper housing, food, bathing facilities and exercise.

Photo by Henri Baré; courtesy of Dr. Leon Whitney

The Racing Homers raised in this Belgian loft are consistent winners.

This elaborate Racing Homer loft is also in Belgium. The owner lives downstairs. The Belgians take their pigeons seriously and raising and racing them is often a full-time task.

HOUSING RACING HOMERS

The loft for Racing Homers should be different from the loft used for housing other breeds. The first requirement for a good racing loft is that it should be elevated so that the pigeons can see it easily from the air. An elevated loft that is easily recognized by the pigeons as soon as they come within sight of it may mean the difference between winning and losing races. The loft should also have a view of the surrounding countryside without the obstruction of other buildings or large trees. Many racing fanciers have met this requirement by constructing their lofts on top of garages or other buildings or even in the attics of their homes. Others, of course, have put up special buildings.

The size of the loft will depend on the number of pigeons you intend to keep. A loft 6 feet wide by 7 feet high by 8 feet deep would adequately house 5 or 6 pairs of Homers. This is a good minimum size for a racing loft. Within certain limits, the more space you can give your pigeons, the better. It is also wise to provide space for more birds than you start with. As time goes on you will undoubtedly want to increase the size of your flock.

Another example of a Belgian racing loft—comfortable and spotless.

This racing loft, also in Belgium, is unusual since most of them are on the top floor of a two-story building.

Divide your loft into three separate compartments: one for stock birds, one for young birds that are being trained and one for the racers. In winter when the birds are not being mated you should separate the sexes. You can do this by dividing each of the three compartments in half by means of solid board partitions so that birds of the opposite sex cannot see each other.

In other respects the loft for Racing Homers should be similar to that provided for other breeds. It should be airy, well-ventilated but not drafty, light, dry, easily cleaned and mouse-proof. You should provide two nest boxes for each pair of pigeons.

Although some Racing Homer lofts have flight pens so that adult birds obtained from other lofts can get some exercise, most of them do not. The birds usually get plenty of exercise outside the loft, in addition to training flights and races. Instead of flight pens, the racing loft is equipped with traps through which the birds can enter the loft but cannot leave. A trap usually consists of a number of straight wires over the entrance which swing inward when a pigeon presses against them but will not swing outward to allow a pigeon to escape. The pigeons can leave only when the trap is raised or opened. Usually there is a small shelf or landing board outside the trap door, on which the pigeon alights before it enters the loft. A very important part of the Racing Homer's training is to enter the loft immediately upon returning home.

This is the home and loft of one of Belgium's best racing pigeon fanciers. He makes an excellent living selling and racing Homers.

This is one of the best English lofts. The English, although more famous for fancy birds than Racing Homers, are world leaders in the pigeon field.

FEEDING RACING HOMERS

The food required by Homers that you are training for the race will vary considerably, depending on climate, season, and the birds' physical condition. Find out what feed mixture experienced fanciers in your area use, and stick to that until you have some experience raising and training Racing Homers. Then you may want to vary the mixture somewhat to suit the needs of your birds.

BREEDING RACING HOMERS

When you pair and mate Racing Homers you apply the same principles used for breeding other types of pigeons, building a strain by carrying out a program of inbreeding, linebreed-

A famous Belgian grizzle Racing Homer.

ing and outcrossing. However, in breeding most varieties of
pigeons you are dealing with more or less tangible physical
characteristics. In breeding Racing Homers the most important
traits are intangible—intelligence, homing instinct and stamina.
Here your own experience and knowledge of the birds' pedi-
grees are most important, and good stock is the prime requisite.

This black checker hen won the First Federation race from Berwick, a 300-mile race which had 8,000 entries. The mother of many winners, she now lives in the United States.

Your racing birds must not be afraid of flying into the coop when you are feeding them. Otherwise they will "shy" when they return from a race and lose precious minutes by failing to enter the loft swiftly.

TAMING RACING HOMERS

If your pigeons are to win races, it is absolutely necessary that they know and trust you. They should be so tame that you can pick any of them up at any time. In order to accomplish this, be gentle with the birds and never make sudden movements while in the loft. Move slowly and deliberately. Feeding by hand, especially if the birds are a little hungry, is one of the best methods of getting your birds tame and familiar with you.

TRAINING RACING HOMERS

Train your pigeons with two purposes in mind. First, the training should develop physical stamina so that the birds will be able to spend hours in the air in all kinds of weather. When the test of the race comes, they should be able to fly the long distances required at top speed and arrive home with some strength and energy in reserve.

The second thing that training should accomplish is to develop to the utmost the latent homing and flying instinct your pigeons have inherited. Again, instinct and ability are there, but

The famous Mr. H. G. Humphrey of London selects a Racing Homer by its "eye-sign."

The inside of a typi cal racing loft, show ing the perches.

they will deteriorate if neglected. There are isolated cases where untrained pigeons have shown remarkable instinct and stamina in returning home from long distances, but they are the exception rather than the rule. If they are trained, your pigeons will provide you with good sport and a great deal of enjoyment.

AGE TRAINING BEGINS

One of the first things the beginning pigeon racing fancier wants to know is at what age he should begin his birds' training flights. There is considerable difference of opinion on this. Some fanciers believe in very early training and take pigeons on their first short training flight when they are about 6 weeks old. Others say the birds should be 3 months old or more before training begins, and still others believe that some intermediate age between these two extremes is best. However, it seems that as long as training begins before the pigeons get too old, the exact age of beginning makes little if any difference. Birds that have not been trained before they are 2 or 3 years old do not make good racers, but birds that are trained within their first year seem to do about the same whether training was begun early or late in that first year.

When training your birds to return to their home, you should also accustom them to being "chucked" from your hand.

Tarzan, a Belgian Racing Homer, has won four first prizes in international races in Europe. It is owned by Andre Van Bruaene.

SETTLING RACING HOMERS

You begin training by settling or "sticking" your pigeons so that they become attached to the home loft and will fly long distances to reach it. This can be quite a problem when you are dealing with adult stock that has been obtained from other fanciers. At the first opportunity the pigeons will return to the loft from which they originally came. If you are buying adult

This female champion English Racing Homer has won many first prizes, including a race in which only champions were competing. She is typical of the English type of Racing Homer, built higher than the usual Belgian Racing Homer.

Another English champion, this blue checker has won 400- and 500-mile races.

Racing Homers, try to get them from someone who lives near you, so it will not be difficult to get them back.

The first step in settling them is to coop them up and to make them as comfortable as possible so that they will become attached to their new surroundings. If you have an aviary or flight cage, encourage the new pigeons to use it. This will help accustom them to the outside of their new home. But don't give them their liberty for about a month.

When you first turn out your new pigeons, they will probably head straight for their old home. They should meet with a cool reception and should not be fed when they get there. They should be handled roughly but not cruelly. When you get them to your loft again, feed and water them and make them feel quite at home. After they have been treated this way several times, turn them out late some afternoon without feeding them. As usual, they will probably head directly for their old home. They should not be allowed to land there but should be waved off. Since they will be getting hungry and night will be fast approaching they will be anxious to find food and shelter as quickly as possible. Back they will go to their new home and the battle will be won.

Obviously this method of settling is only possible when you have obtained your birds from someone in your immediate locality. If your birds come from a loft some distance away it will be harder to settle them. In such a case about the only successful settling method is to keep the pigeons cooped up for several months. Release them only after they have raised several nests of young, and while they are feeding newly hatched squabs.

When carrying pigeons on the roof of your car on training trips, be sure that they are protected from the wind and flying particles that might injure their eyes.

When you train your Racing Homers, you must "walk" them through the "bucking bars" so they won't waste time entering the loft immediately after they return from a race. If they become hungry during their flight, they will be anxious to return home as quickly as possible.

Even so, there is no guarantee that you will not lose them. By far the safest course is to use such birds only for breeding purposes and to train the squabs they produce.

RETURNING TO THE LOFT

The hardest part of training young birds is to get them accustomed to the exterior of their loft so they will recognize it from the air. The best way to do this is to place them on the roof of the loft before they are strong enough to do much flying. After a few such outings they will begin to fly around a bit and will soon be taking short flights in the vicinity of the loft. After this you may let them out two or three times daily to fly around and get some exercise. The youngsters must also be trained to return through the trap door. You may first let them perch on the landing board for a while. When they re-enter the loft through the trap, give them a little food by hand and praise them. If they hesitate to re-enter through the trap after they have been flying around for a while, you can rattle some grain around to tempt them. Never let them stop on trees, other roofs or telephone wires. If you are kind and patient, they will soon understand that they must return immediately to the loft.

TRAINING FLIGHTS

When your young pigeons have reached this stage, you may take them away from the loft on their first training flight. First, it is a good idea to familiarize them with the basket in which you will carry them to the release point. (Baskets are available from pigeon suppliers or pet dealers.) Put the young birds in the basket several times before you take them out for their first flight. Keep them in the basket for an hour or so. Many authorities recommend putting the birds in the basket the night before their first training flight and having them spend the night in it. The basket, by the way, should have a water trough attached to it so the birds may be given a drink before their release. But they should not be fed immediately before a training flight or race.

On the day of the flight, start out early in the morning before the sun is too hot. Take the pigeons in their basket to a point about a mile (or perhaps a little less) from the loft and release them. If you are training your birds for a particular race or group of races, the release point should be on the same route they will follow during the race.

A day or two later take the birds two miles away, in the same direction, and, for the third lesson, five miles. Gradually increase the distance that the birds are required to fly until they are covering as much as 70 or 80 miles or more. Since many of the races for young pigeons are approximately 70 miles, it is a good idea to train them up to this point. Some experienced fanciers maintain that it is best occasionally to change the direction from which the birds are released so that they will become familiar with the terrain surrounding the loft from every point of the compass and will thus be less easily confused when they are in actual races later.

After the young pigeons have reached the 10-mile stage in their training, release the birds individually rather than in groups, letting them cover the same ground they've already been over. This helps develop the self-confidence the birds will need when they are racing. There may not always be a group from the home loft, and the birds should learn to strike out on their own instead of following others. Some fanciers recommend always releasing the young birds singly or in twos instead of in groups on training flights. They argue that if two birds are released together they immediately start for home instead of wasting valuable time circling. But mated pairs should never be sent on the same training flight or race. Part of the incentive to return home quickly is the desire to return to the absent mate. Parent pigeons, incidentally, are excellent racers, with the hens especially fast. But don't send a parent out when eggs are about to hatch or squabs have just been born. Similarly, it is not a good idea to race birds during the molt. During this time

This Racing Homer, back from a race, enters through the trap. Many races are won at the coop, since birds often fly together from the release point back to their home town. The winner is thus the bird that is trained to enter the coop without lingering on the roof.

they have less endurance and may lose their flight feathers. For that reason, races for older pigeons are held in spring and early summer, and the younger birds race in the autumn.

As you are training your pigeons you will, of course, observe their individual characteristics. Notice which ones show a highly developed homing instinct and great speed. Those are the ones you will want to enter in fairly short races that call for swiftness. The pigeons that evidence great stamina are suited for the longer endurance races. Racing Homers have been known to fly a mile a minute for 300 miles. Although the ultimate in pigeon racing is to have a winner in one of the long-distance races (500-600 miles or more) you should content yourself with training your birds for the shorter races for a year or so, until you have some experience and have developed and trained some 2- or 3-year-old birds that are capable of long-distance flying.

THE RACE

After you have thoroughly trained your pigeons, you are ready to enter them in their first race. Take them to the appointed place the night before the race. Here they are marked with a numbered race band or ring. Other pigeon racing enthusiasts with their birds will be there and most of them will have a piece of indispensable equipment—a time clock. This is an instrument that records the exact time of arrival of each pigeon from the race. When a pigeon returns home the numbered race band or ring that has been put on his leg is immediately removed and inserted in the clock and the lever is pulled. This automatically prints the exact time on a roll of paper in the clock or pricks it on a paper dial. The clock is then turned in at racing headquarters and the judges open it to find the winner.

Obviously, particularly in the short-distance races, a bird cannot win a race until he has entered the loft and his owner has removed the band from his leg and inserted it in the time

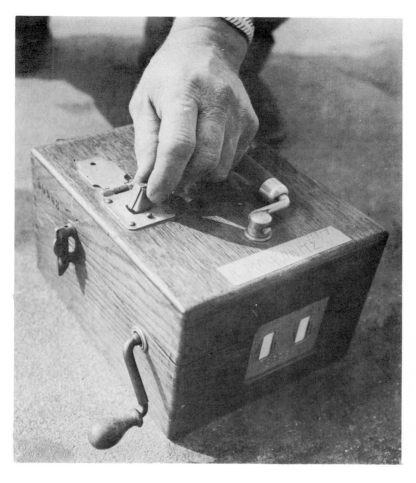

As soon as the band comes off the Racing Homer's leg, it goes into the time clock.

Here the top of the racing clock is open to show its workings.

clock. That is why it is so important to train your pigeons not only to fly straight home in the shortest possible time but to enter the loft immediately upon arriving. Many races have been lost because of pigeons that lingered outside the loft after arriving home. However, since they are mostly creatures of habit, if you train your birds at an early age to go through the trap, they will continue to do so. You might always keep them a little hungry when they are on training and racing flights and scatter a few grains of feed inside the trap. When your birds return home and enter the trap be sure that you don't treat them roughly or scare them in your eagerness to get the band off and into the time clock. Treat them kindly and gently, since rough treatment will only serve to make them reluctant to enter the loft in the future.

CARRYING MESSAGES

Once your pigeons' homing instinct has been developed, it is a simple matter for you to get them to carry messages home, if you wish. The message goes into a light, plastic capsule that fastens to the band on the leg. During the war pigeons carried films and maps in special containers that fit into a harness which went over the shoulders, under the wings and across the breast.

TRAINING FANCY PIGEONS

Training fancy flying pigeons differs according to the type of pigeons you have and what you wish to train them to do. In spite of this, however, all the fancy pigeons have a great deal in common and, except for their specialties—high flying, rolling, and so forth—all require basically the same training.

As a general rule most of the fancy flyers are not nearly as hard to stick or settle in their new lofts as are Racing Homers. Usually good treatment for a week or two and the opportunity to get thoroughly acquainted with their new home, both inside and out, is all that is necessary. In particularly obstinate cases the method used to settle Racing Homers (p. 114) may be used. After your birds have been thoroughly settled, the most important lesson for you to teach them is to return to the loft when signalled to do so. They should also know that they must not alight on other roofs or eaves.

Again, the type of pigeons you have will in a measure determine the length of time they will want to be in the air and the difficulty that you will have in bringing them down. All pigeons, however, can be taught to return at a given signal. The signal may be anything you wish to use—a ringing bell, a waving stick, etc.—as long as the pigeons come to associate it with feeding-time. Sometimes, particularly with long- and high-flying pigeons such as Flying Tipplers, other pigeons, called "droppers" or "chicos," are used to signal the flying pigeons down. The birds soon learn to return to the loft upon the appearance of a White Fantail, Nun, or some other pigeon that does not fly far but stays close to the loft.

With pigeons that do not fly far but circle above the loft, one very effective method of training them to return is to keep them fairly hungry. Don't feed them before they are turned out for a flight. They soon learn that they will be fed after they have flown for a short time and they watch for your appearance. When you begin to throw seed they will come right home.

How often you let your pigeons fly will depend on several factors. The temperature and weather will, of course, have some bearing on it. Pigeons seem to fly better, enjoy it more, and tire less in cool weather than in hot. When it is cool, your birds may fly daily. In very hot weather, three or four times a week should be sufficient. During the molt many birds seem to have little desire to fly and should not be forced. It is also unwise to fly a hen that is about to lay as she may strain herself and cause permanent damage. Some fanciers advise against flying pigeons during the time when they are feeding squabs less than 10 days old, but except with Long Rolling Rollers, it seems to do no harm.

Once pigeons become accustomed to flying at a certain time of day they seem to prefer to fly at that time regularly instead of at different times on different days. A set schedule seems to mean a great deal.

Remember that the rolling and tumbling variations exhibited by the Rollers and Tumblers are part of their inheritance. Giving them the opportunity to perform will keep their inbred skill keen.

This blue-barred Racing Homer is another famous English champion.

Gallery

Photo on page 135 by Dr. Herbert R. Axelrod. Bird owned by TFH Publications, Inc.

Photos on bottom of page 155 and bottom of page 159, by the owner, Ralph Buch-Brage. Courtesy of Mr. Buch-Brage.

Photo on page 142 by the owner, Paul S. Muhlmann. Courtesy of Mr. Muhlmann.

Photo on page 143 by the owner, George Neuerburg. Courtesy of Mr. Neuerburg.

Photos on pages 129, 130, bottom 131, 134, 139, 140 (top and bottom), 141, 145, 146, 147, 148, top 155, 156 and 158 by R. L. Kienlen. All reproduced courtesy of Ralston Purina Company. Birds owned by H. Eric Buri, Julien Jeanguenin, Orman Forcht, Harry Granger, Victor Eshpeter, Joe Frazier, Dr. Sam Peavey, J. Norman High, L. F. Rue, Thornton's Birds & Bantams, Robert Pommer, Hubert Rieth, Dr. L. E. Hummel, R. K. Wagner, Walter F. Werkheiser—in that order.

Photos on top of page 131, pages 132, 136, 137, 144, 149, 150, 152, 153, 154, 157, top 159 by Stauber. Birds owned by H. Bartschi, Hans Mannlein, Franz Hackl, Stefan Kellermann, Peter Rolli, Karl Zausinger, Wilhelm Henkel, Heinrich Ruzicka, Oswald Weber, F. Spahr, Adrian Bigger, Hans Blum—in that order.

Photo on page 138 by Thakkar. Bird owned by Commodore His Highness Maharajah Raol Shri Krishnakumarsinhji (Bhavnagar, India).

Photos on pages 133 and 151 by Van Gink. Courtesy of Van Gink. Birds owned by N. Alsemgeest and S. De Zoete, respectively.

Miniature American Crest: This cream young hen is a member of a strictly exhibition breed, approximately 30 years in existence. Among its ancestors are the Long-Faced Tumblers and the Modena. American in origin, the Miniature Crest is not widely found except in the New Jersey area.

Antwerp breed: Another strictly exhibition breed, but one of note-worthy hardiness. Plain-headed and having no fancy ornaments, the Antwerps are nevertheless a striking breed. Here you see a blue-barred cock. The body build testifies to its descendance from the Belgian Homing Pigeon. Most Antwerps have red eyes.

(Above) Archangel: Lustre and sheen are the main characteristics. Here, a blue-winged (barless) cock. (Below) Barb: A famous exhibition breed, with black or dun coloration the most-prized. Here, an all-black cock.

Scandaroon: An elite fancier's breed, found among those pigeon-men who like the unusual. A tall, erect, tight-feathered breed that is kept for exhibition only. Other distinguishing characteristics are the well-developed eye cere, beak wattle, and scythe-shaped beak. Here you see a white cock.

Old Dutch Capuchine: An exhibition breed with an attractive hood that does not cover the bird's head, thus distinguishing it from the Jacobin. Once thought to be extinct, the breed was re-discovered about 25 years ago in its homeland, the Netherlands, and is now thriving. Here you see a yellow Old Dutch Capuchine—a young hen. Contrast its chain with that of a Jacobin.

English Carrier: Once used for carrying messages, this breed is today strictly an exhibition bird. It is one of the tallest breeds in existence and characterized by well-developed eye ceres and large, walnut-shaped beak wattles. For over a century this breed was the most popular pigeon in England, where Asiatic fanciers developed it from the Baghdad pigeon. Here you see an all-black cock.

American Domestic Flight: This breed comes in two classes, plain-headed and crested. It is a small, light bird with white eyes. New York fanciers created this breed some time about 1880. Its ancestors include the Magpie pigeon, the Hamburg white-tailed Tumbler and the Hanover white-eyed Tumbler. Until 1928 it was a purely flying bird. Today, you will find many in shows. Here you see a beautifully crested bronze-mottled cock. This particular bird is a flyer.

Florentine: Once producer of the choicest table squabs in Europe, it looks like a magnified Gazzi Modena (one of its ancestors). Adult birds average 24–28 ounces. A blue-checkered young hen here.

Frillback: The most outstanding feature of this breed is the backwards-curling or "frilled" body feathers and coverts; these make the bird look much larger than its usual 13–14 ounces. An exceptionally unusual breed, these pigeons are thought to have originated in Asia Minor. The short legs are usually adorned with either grouses or small boots. Note the boots on this blue grizzled cock.

Indian Gola: A flying bird that must be tethered to its coop during shows. Many colors and color patterns. Crosses easily with other breeds and has contributed its blood to several popular Mondaines.

Helmet: This breed boasts all-white plumage except for the upper portion of its head—and the effect of these particular colored feathers gives the breed its name. Can be either crested or plain-headed; long-, short- or medium-faced. For centuries one of Europe's most popular flying pigeons. Today many fanciers prefer to use it as a coopie, or decoy bird, to bring racing pigeons down. Here you see a cock with black helmet and a crest.

(Above) American Giant Racing Homer: This Andalusian-blue cock belongs to a breed created in America c. 1920 and raised for show and food. (Below) Hungarian: Breed with noticeably proud carriage. Raised for show—and sometimes food. Here, a red cock.

Ice Pigeon: This breed's pale ice-blue color is extremely unusual among pigeons and gives the breed both its name and its most distinguishing characteristic. It is always plain-headed, but comes in two leg types: clean and muffed. Originating in Saxony and Silesia, it belongs to the German Toy Group and averages 12½–13½ ounces. Here you see a white-checkered hen of the clean-legged type. White-checkered Ice Pigeons are also called either "white-laced" or "spangled."

Jacobin: A Jacobin's head is completely hidden except when you trim its hood to permit it to raise and feed its young. At other times of the year it can barely see because of its splendid hood and chain feathers. Its ornate feathering makes the Jacobin look much larger than its usual 16 ounces. Considered delicate, it is usually raised only by élite, but devoted, fanciers (among them Queen Victoria). Here, a yellow cock. Note the clean legs that are another characteristic of the breed.

142

King: a strictly American breed, with different colors originating in different states. A dual-purpose breed raised for both squab-food (young birds often weigh 34 ounces) and exhibition. Here, a khaki-colored young hen. Most khaki Kings, however, are slimmer and browner than this particular bird.

English Magpie: A slender, erect, and stylishly balanced breed, developed from the German Magpie and French Baghdad by English fanciers who wanted a bird of more elegant style. A strictly exhibition bird averaging 14–16 ounces despite its height. Here, a black young cock. Note the characteristic, and pleasing, balance of all the parts: beak, head, neck, body, wings and tail.

Gazzi Modena: One of the most popular pigeons in America, the Modena comes in 152 color varieties and two basic patterns. Here, a young bronze Gazzi Modena hen. The other color pattern—the Schietti Modena—lacks the Gazzi's striking white plumage. *The* flying pigeon of medieval Italy, Modenas are today show-birds and also in great demand as decoy birds to land racing pigeons. Note how every part of the Modena's body is based on a graceful curve.

Jewel Mondaine: Extremely rare pigeon because it is so difficult to produce a pure white bird with even black tigering (or mottling) that can breed true for several generations. The Jewel Mondaine has been in existence only since 1946 when an American fancier managed to cross a White Swiss Mondaine with a black French Mondaine to get the dramatic mottling he wanted. However, a club has been organized to nurture this breed. Here, a black-tigered cock.

Nun: Affectionate, soft-feathered bird today raised for show and companionship rather than for flying ability. Nuns should have pearl eyes and, usually, they weigh no more than 13 ounces. Here you see a red cock. Note the characteristic shell-type crest.

Blondinette Oriental Frill: "Blondinette" refers to the color pattern of this pigeon variety. It has no white in its plumage while the Satinette, the other major variety of Oriental Frill, has a white head and body. Blondinettes and Satinettes both make excellent coopies and showbirds, but have little flying ability. Here, a silver-laced Blondinette cock. Note the short beak and ornamental neck feathering (frill).

Bavarian Pouter: Breed still in the process of creation. (Its show-standard is still provisional.) This show-bird was first developed as late as 1960 by crossing Bohemian pigeons, Pomeranian croppers and the English Pouters. (Note the crop resemblance to the last.) Upright carriage and high stance are the characteristics that breeders interested in this as yet unfinished pigeon variety are trying to develop. Here, a blue-checkered cock.

Hessian Pouter: Formerly a free-flying bird raised by Hessian peas-
ants, this breed has been since 1920 an exhibition bird. It has the
full-blown crop of all Pouters, averages 18 to 19 ounces in weight,
and has no ornaments except its many colors and color variations.
Here, a blue-checkered hen.

Old Holland Pouter: Sometimes called the "Dutch Cropper," this breed is believed to be the oldest variety of Pouter in Europe. Of unknown origin in some Eastern country, not even the exact date of its importation into Holland is known. The Dutch cropper is almost certainly the ancestor of the English Pouter and the other Pouter breeds. Here, a black-mottled cock. Note the characteristic large and ornate leg muffs and tall, erect appearance.

Franconian Velvet-Shield: An exhibition breed valued chiefly for its glossy plumage. The unusual "grease quills" running from the bird's tail to the wing on each side are believed to be responsible for the exceptional glossiness. Other characteristics are small size (average weight: 12–14 ounces) and the red eye cere. Comes in many colors and color patterns. Here you see a brown-checkered hen. Only two flight feathers should participate in these birds' shield pattern.

152

White-Tailed Starling: Despite their scanty 12½–13½ ounces, Starlings are a strong, flying breed whose members can easily forage and fend for themselves in country fields. They are classified into at least 10 formal varieties according to their color markings. Here, a black hen of the White-Tailed-Starling variety.

Strasser: Mainly an exhibition and food-producing breed. Some breeders cross it with King pigeons to make their Strassers larger, blockier and shorter. Note the similarity of its color pattern to that of the Gazzi Modena. Here a blue, white-barred cock.

(Above) Bohemian Fairy (Tiger) Swallow: Very scarce for the same reason as is the Jewel Mondaine. Note the large, ornate muff and how both muff feathers and wing feathers alternate in color. (Below) Egyptian Swift: A little-known breed—here a mealy (Ootati) cock.

Syrian Swift: Somewhat smaller and tighter of feather than the Egyptian Swift, but still bearing a marked resemblance to it. (Note the long wings and tail plus the short legs and small feet that give the Swifts a low, squat appearance: the Swifts are totally different in appearance from all other existing pigeon varieties.) The Syrian Swift was probably imported into that country from Egypt and, in its new home, was cultivated as a flying pigeon. Here you see a young cock, spread-indigo. Note the wings that will give it a formidable wing-span.

German Trumpeter: A strictly exhibition bird with very short legs that bring it strikingly close to the floor. The rose is hardly ever developed but, instead, grows forward over the nostrils in the form of a reverse tuft of feathers. Thus Trumpeters have a *beak crest,* and some are double crested (have both a beak crest plus a crest at the top of the head). Here, a beak-crested, silver-checkered cock. Note also the ornate leg muffs. Another, and distinct, variety of Trumpeter—the Dresden Trumpeter—was used to breed the hard-to-achieve Bohemian Fairy Swallow (Tiger Swallow).

Show Tippler: An exhibition breed developed in England by fanciers who wanted to enter their Flying Tipplers in show-competitions. Archangels, Brands, and other pigeons were then crossed to produce the Show Tippler. It differs from its flyer ancestors in that more attention is paid to the roundness of the bird's head, the eye-color, the depth of color, and the color arrangement of the feathers. There are four main color patterns with chuck (all-white plumage with only colored primaries and tail feathers) being the rarest. Here you see a light-mottled bronze hen.

(Above) Oriental Roller: A flying and rolling (performing) breed rarely seen in the show-rooms. Dun cock. (Below) A "Silky" or mutant Sedosa hen with lacy, ostrichlike plumage. Silkies can be brought about in every breed; such birds cannot fly.

Index